AQA

GCSE Science

ADDITIONAL APPLIED

Editor: Stewart Chenery

John Atkinson
Stewart Chenery
Sally Goodwin
Claire Moody

Hodder Murray

A MEMBER OF THE HODDER HEADLINE GROUP

The Publishers would like to thank the following for permission to reproduce copyright material:

Photo credits

p.2 *l* Getty Images/Simon Wilkinson, *r* Empics/David Jones/PA; **p.3** *l* Empics/Phil Noble/PA, *r* Empics/DPA; **p.4** *t* Sony UK Limited, *c* Andrew Lambert Photography, *b* Last Resort Picture Library; **p.6** *c* © Lester Lefkowitz/Corbis, *b* © Chris Bland; Eye Ubiquitous/Corbis; **p.7** *t* © John Hulme; Eye Ubiquitous/Corbis, *c* Copyright © Nokia, 2005; **p.9** *t* Science Photo Library/Adam Gault, *b* Science Photo Library/Mauro Fermariello; **p.10** Getty Images/Wide Group; **p.11** *c* Still Pictures/Robert Holmgren, *b* Gouhier Nicolas/Abaca/Empics; **p.12** *l* Empics/John Harrell/AP, *c* Corbis/Shepard Sherbell, *cr* Science Photo Library/Tek Image; **p.13** Empics/John Giles/PA; **p.17** *l* Science Photo Library/Tek Image, *r* Corbis; **p.18** Science Photo Library; **p.26** Last Resort Picture Library; **p.28** Rex Features/Burger/Phanie; **p.29** John Heseltine/Science Photo Library; **p.30** Science Photo Library/John McLean; **p.31** *all* Shout/John Callan; **p.32** Alamy/John McKay/Elvele; **p.33** *t* Photo Courtesy of Chiltern International Fire, *b* Courtesy British Automatic Sprinkler Association; **p.35** *l* Science Photo Library/Philippe Psaila, *r* Empics/Rui Vieira/PA; **p.37** *l* Science Photo Library/Pascal Goetgheluck, *r* Still Pictures/Ullstein-Grabowsky; **p.39** *t* Lorna Ainger, *b* Getty Images/Roberto Schmidt; **p.40** *cl* Lorna Ainger, *cr* Science Photo Library/Cordelia Molloy, *b* Getty Images/Burgess Blevins; **p.41** Getty Images/Johner; **p.42** *t* Anthony Blake Photo Library/Maximilian Stock Ltd., *cl* Science Photo Library/ Professors P.M. Motta, T. Fujita & M. Muto, *bl* Science Photo Library/David Munns; **p.44** *c* Alamy/Medical-on-Line, *b* Science Photo Library/Biophoto Associates; **p.45** *t* Science Photo Library/Biophoto Associates, *b* Corbis/Photocuisine; **p.46** Lorna Ainger; **p.48** Science Photo Library/Andrew McClenaghan; **p.51** *t* Corbis/Photocuisine, *b* Science Photo Library/Cordelia Molloy; **p.57** Lorna Ainger; **p.61** Science Photo Library/Martyn F. Chillmaid; **p.65** Cephas/Stockfood; **p.68** Corbis/David Raymer; **p.71** Science Photo Library/Philippe Psaila; **p.72** Science Photo Library/BSIP, Beranger; **p.74** Science Photo Library/John Durham; **p.79** Alamy/Picture Partners; **p.80** Alamy/Nigel Cattlin/Holt; **p.82** Alamy/David Hoffman Photo Library; **p.83** Alamy/Per Karlsson - BKWine.com; **p.91** *l* Empics/Rui Vieira/PA, *r* Science Photo Library/Michael Donne; **p.92** Rex Features/Today; **p.93** Getty Images/Romeo Gacad/AFP; **p.95** Corbis/Ashley Cooper; **p.96** *t* Science Photo Library/Michael Donne, *b* Science Photo Library/Tek Image; **p.97** *c* Science Photo Library/Mauro Fermariello, *b* Science Photo Library/Michael Donne; **p.98** Science Photo Library/Pascal Goetgheluck; **p.99** Corbis/Charles O'Rear; **p.101** Courtesy Centrex; **p.102** *t* Science Photo Library/ Mauro Fermariello, *c* Getty Images/Stuart McClymont; **p.103** Science Photo Library/Mauro Fermariello, *b* Science Photo Library/Charles D. Winters; **p.109** *t* Science Photo Library/Jerry Mason, *b* Corbis/David Sutherland; **p.112** *t* Science Photo Library/Andrew Lambert, *b* Science Photo Library/Martyn F. Chillmaid; **p.115** *c* Science Photo Library/Steve Horrell, *b* Rex Features/Dave Penman; **p.116** Rex Features/Jonathan Hordle; **p.118** Science Photo Library/Andrew Lambert; **p.124** Science Photo Library/J.C. Revy; **p.127** Shout/John Callan; **p.128** Science Photo Library/Adam Hart-Davis; **p.130** Courtesy Ann Lee Davis, Department of Forensic Science Richmond, Virginia; **p.132** *l* Science Photo Library/Eye of Science, *cl* Science Photo Library/Susumu Nishinaga, *cr* Science Photo Library/R.E. Litchfield, *r* Science Photo Library/Dr. G.D. Danilatos; **p.133** Corbis/Micro Discovery; **p.137** Empics/PA; **p.141** Alamy/Ian Miles-Flashpoint Pictures; **p.142** Rex Features; **p.146** *l* Andrew Syred/Science Photo Library, *c* Getty Images/Stock4B, *r* Lorna Ainger; **p.147** Getty Images/Phil Walter; **p.148** Science Photo Library; **p.150** Science Photo Library/Andrew Syred; **p.153** Prof. P. Motta/ Dept. of Anatomy/ University "La Sapienza", Rome; **p.156** Courtesy Human Performance Laboratory, Ball State University; **p.157** *t* Corbis/Pete Saloutos, *b* Action Plus/Neil Tingle; **p.160** Corbis; **p.161** Getty Images/Axel Thomae; **p.163** Science Photo Library/Steve Gschmeissner; **p.164** Getty Images/Altrendo; **p.166** Science Photo Library/Maximilian Stock Ltd; **p.167** Corbis/Christian Liewig/Liewig Media Sports; **p.170** *c* Getty Images/Al Bello, *b* Empics/Steve Mitchell; **p.171** Getty Images/Javier Soriano; **p.175** Corbis; **p.176** Courtesy Patterson-Medical; **p.177** *tl* Alamy/Tetra Images, *tr* Getty Images/Marc Romanelli, *c* Courtesy Acuflex/Power Systems, Inc; **p.179** Rex Features/Nils Jorgensen; **p.181** Alamy/Mike Dobel; **p.182** Getty Images/Joerg Koch/AFP; **p.183** *c* Courtesy 2006 BMW Motorrad, *b* Getty Images/David Rogers; **p.184** *c* Corbis/Aly Song/Reuters, *b* Courtesy Adidas; **p.185** *c* Getty Images/Roger Viollet, *b* Getty Images/Timothy A. Clary/AFP; **p.186** *t* Corbis/Marc Lecureuil, *c* Alamy/Rodolfo Arpia; **p.189** *t* Action images, *bl* Alamy/Robert Morris, *br* Getty Images/Cesar Rangel/AFP; **p.191** *bl* Topfoto/Roger-Viollet, *br* Getty Images/Franck Fife/AFP; **p.192** Getty Images/Vladimir Rys/Bongarts; **p.193** Getty Images/Johannes Simon/AFP.

t: top, *b*: bottom, *l*: left, *r*: right, *c*: centre

Acknowledgements

p.14 The Health and Safety Executive for permission to use their company logo; **p.25** St. John Ambulance, St. Andrew's Ambulance Association and the British Red Cross for permission to use their organisation logos; **p.81** The Soil Association for permission to use their company logo – The Soil Association's organic symbol is a guarantee that food carrying it is produced to the highest standard of organic animal welfare and environmental protection; **p.164** Body of evidence, Copyright Guardian Newspapers Limited 2005. Author: Vivienne Parry; **p.174** Train like a Lion, Copyright Guardian Newspapers Limited 2005. Author: Paul Doyle; **p.193** Oi, Faster!, Copyright Guardian Newspapers Limited 2005. Author: Alok Jha.

Every effort has been made to trace all copyright holders, but if any have been inadvertently overlooked the Publishers will be pleased to make the necessary arrangements at the first opportunity.

Although every effort has been made to ensure that website addresses are correct at time of going to press, Hodder Murray cannot be held responsible for the content of any website mentioned in this book. It is sometimes possible to find a relocated web page by typing in the address of the home page for a website in the URL window of your browser.

Risk Assessment

As a service to our users, a risk assessment for this text has been carried out by CLEAPSS and is available on request to the publishers. However, the publishers accept no legal responsibility on any issue arising from this risk assessment: whilst every effort has been made to check the instructions of practical work in this book, it is still the duty and legal obligation of schools to carry out their own risk assessments.

Hodder Headline's policy is to use papers that are natural, renewable and recyclable products and made from wood grown in sustainable forests. The logging and manufacturing processes are expected to conform to the environmental regulations of the country of origin.

Orders: please contact Bookpoint Ltd, 130 Milton Park, Abingdon, Oxon OX14 4SB. Telephone: (44) 01235 827720. Fax: (44) 01235 400454. Lines are open 9.00 – 5.00, Monday to Saturday, with a 24-hour message answering service. Visit our website at www.hoddereducation.co.uk

© John Atkinson, Stewart Chenery, Sally Goodwin, Claire Moody 2006
First published in 2006 by
Hodder Murray, an imprint of Hodder Education,
a member of the Hodder Headline Group
338 Euston Road
London NW1 3BH

Impression number   5 4 3 2 1
Year   2010 2009 2008 2007 2006

Cover photo Photodisc
Illustrations by Barking Dog Art
Typeset in 11.5pt Times by Fakenham Photosetting Limited, Fakenham, Norfolk
Printed in Italy

A catalogue record for this title is available from the British Library

ISBN-10: 0340 907 126
ISBN-13: 978 0 34090712 2

Contents

Introduction

This book is designed to cover the specification leading to the AQA GCSE award in **Additional Applied Science.** The course is principally about what food, forensic and sports scientists do, the skills they need and the way in which they work. The course will also give you the opportunity to investigate other types of work where scientific skills are used. The Additional Applied Science course also will concentrate on some important health and safety issues associated with scientific workplaces.

The course is divided into three units:

Unit 1 Science in the workplace	20% of the total marks
Unit 2 Science at work	40% of the total marks
Unit 3 Using scientific skills	40% of the total marks

Assessment of the course

Your teachers will assess your work in **Units 1** and **3. Unit 2** will be assessed by a written examination. The examination will be available at two tiers and you will need to discuss with your teacher the appropriate level for you. It is important that you read the specifications for the course; these will tell you exactly what you have to learn and what you have to do.

In **Units 1** and **3** you must put together a folder of work. For **Unit 1** your folder must contain evidence that you have studied the use of science and scientific skills in the workplace. Your folder should also contain evidence that you appreciate the importance of health and safety both in the workplace and in the laboratory.

Your folder should contain:
- a report of an investigation on workplaces that use scientific skills, describing the work of scientists or those that use scientific skills and how science is important in a wide variety of jobs;
- a report of an investigation carried out into working safely in a scientific workplace and a comparison with the health and safety precautions in your school or college.

In **Units 2** and **3** you will study some of the knowledge required and the tasks carried out by food, forensic and sports scientists. You will also be given the opportunity to use some of the skills of these scientists; these units may well be taught together.

Unit 2 will be examined under examination conditions and you will be required to answer questions on:
- Food science
- Forensic science
- Sports science.

Only work from this unit will be examined and you will need to revise this carefully in preparation for the examination. The examination lasts for one hour and will contain questions that are set in an applied context. These questions will be concerned with the application of science, for example:
- the type of diet recommended by a dietician for a diabetic person;
- how a scenes-of-crime officer (SOCO) would collect certain types of evidence from a crime scene for later analysis by a forensic scientist;
- how a sports scientist may design a fitness campaign for a particular sports person.

For **Unit 3** your folder must contain evidence that you have successfully used some of the scientific skills used by food, forensic or sports scientists during your course. You will need to submit **one** complete investigation.

Your folder should contain a record of investigations or techniques used by one of these scientists in which you should:
- describe the purpose of the investigation;
- include a plan and risk assessment for the investigation;
- include data collected from the investigation;
- make conclusions from, and evaluate, the investigation;
- explain how the particular scientist might use the results of the investigation.

This book is divided into five chapters that contain the material necessary to complete the three units of the course. Each unit is divided into sections or topics in which you will find specific learning points from the specification.

Chapters 1 and 2 deal with science in the workplace and contain the material you will need to include in your folder for unit 1.

Chapters 3, 4 and 5 contain the information on the knowledge and skills used by food, forensic and sports scientists. The learning points explain what you need to know for the Unit 2 examination or, in the case of Unit 3, what you need to do and include in your folder of work.

Throughout the book, you will find questions to complete that have been designed so that you may both check and extend your knowledge and understanding. End-of-chapter questions are also included throughout Unit 2. You will find that key scientific words have been identified and explained in Glossary boxes.

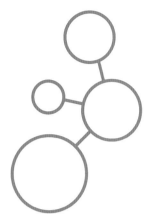

Unit 1
Science in the workplace

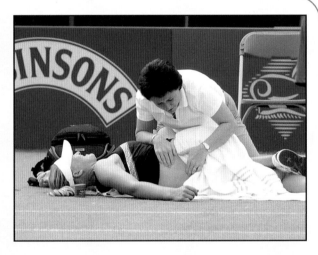

Unit 1 is divided into two chapters:

Chapter 1   Investigating how science is used

Chapter 2   Working safely in science

In this unit you will learn about the types of industry and businesses that use science and scientific skills. You will also learn about some people that use scientific knowledge and skills in their work and find out about the types of job that they have and what exactly they do.

Also in this unit you learn about the importance of health and safety in science and what to do in the case of an accident. You will need to compare the health and safety procedures found in an industry or business with those in your school or college.

The work that you complete for this unit will be assessed by your teacher and form part of the portfolio of work required to complete the Additional Applied Science course.

Chapter 1
Investigating how science is used

Chapter 1 is divided into four topics:

1. The importance of science in everyday life
2. Investigating organisations that use science
3. Investigating the roles of scientists and those who use science
4. Health and safety in scientific workplaces

In this section of Unit 1 you need to produce a report of an investigation on workplaces that use scientific skills, describing the work of scientists or those who use scientific skills, and how science is important in a wide variety of jobs.

Your teacher will assess this section of the course as part of your coursework. While completing your report, you will need to use the statements at the beginning of each topic as a guide to the information you should include. You will also need to use the Unit 1 assessment grid in the AQA Additional Applied Science specification. The assessment grid is divided into three stages. The checklist below details what should be included at each stage.

To reach Stage 1, you should be able to produce a report that states clearly the purpose of a range of organisations (minimum of three) that use science or scientific skills, and identify the jobs of those employed.

To get higher marks, you should be able to describe the organisations as local, national or international and give their location. You should be able to describe clearly the products or services, together with the jobs and qualifications of those working with science or using scientific skills. You should also be able to outline the types of career available in science.

❶ Make a list of as many industries as you can think of where you may find a scientist at work.

The highest marks will be awarded if you include a more detailed account of one of the organisations, including reasons for its location. You should be able to describe particular skills of the people working in the organisation, as well as the importance of the organisation to society and its effects on the local environment.

Synthetic
A material that does not occur naturally, but is made by people (or machines)

Figure 1.1 An MP3 player

Figure 1.2 Materials scientists design materials for packaging.

Figure 1.3 Chemists are involved in the production of toiletries and cosmetics.

1 The importance of science in everyday life

When completing your report for Unit 1 you will need to:
- identify local, national and international businesses and service providers that use science;
- find out where the organisations are located and why.

The science industry is one of the most important industries contributing to the national economy. The success of the national economy is often judged by the output of the science industry. The science industry contributes to many things that we may take for granted.

Most of the science studied in this course will be concerned with the work of food, forensic and sports scientists. However, science contributes to your everyday life in many ways, whether you are shopping, playing football, painting your bedroom or watching a film. You may be sitting in a chair that is made of plastic or perhaps filled with fire-resistant foam. Your chair may be covered with a material that is **synthetic** and developed by a part of the science industry.

In your room you may have a television, hi-fi, MP3 or DVD player, all produced by the electronics industry.

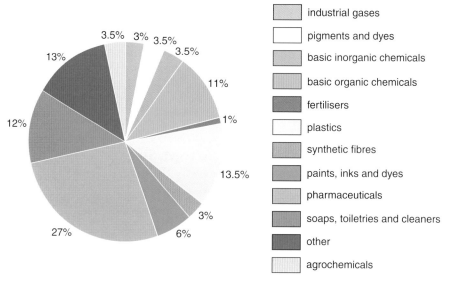

industrial gases
pigments and dyes
basic inorganic chemicals
basic organic chemicals
fertilisers
plastics
synthetic fibres
paints, inks and dyes
pharmaceuticals
soaps, toiletries and cleaners
other
agrochemicals

3.5% 3% 3.5%
13% 3.5%
11%
12% 1%
13.5%
27% 3%
6%

Figure 1.4 Products made by the chemical industry

2 What does the pharmaceutical industry produce?

3 What type of scientist might be found in the pharmaceutical industry?

4 What are agrochemicals?

5 Suggest where you might find industrial gases being used.

6 Give the names of four man-made fibres.

Perhaps you have just had a snack or a drink – produced by the food industry and developed by food scientists. Materials scientists will have produced the materials for the snack containers and drink cans.

When you take a shower, shampoo your hair, clean your teeth and use some cosmetics, you are using products that have been developed by cosmetic scientists.

A good example of the wide range of products produced by scientists can be found in the chemical industry. The pie chart in Figure 1.4 gives the range of products produced by the chemical industry.

Some of the materials in Figure 1.4 are used as ingredients for other chemical products, such as pharmaceuticals, paints and personal hygiene goods, many of which are purchased directly by the consumer. However, about half the chemical materials and products made are purchased directly by industries and form vital ingredients for the

Figure 1.5 Locations of the main areas of employment in the chemical industry

products and services they provide. All chemicals end up being used in products and services purchased by the consumer, but there may be many stages between the sale of a chemical and the final consumer product. Car manufacturers make direct purchases of chemicals (such as paints), but also buy plastic, rubber, textile and electronic components, which rely on other chemical materials.

On average, it is estimated that each UK household either directly or indirectly spends £25–30 per week on chemicals in one form or other.

Science-based industries or those that use science may be found almost anywhere, but a number of questions are normally considered before a final decision is taken on the location, including:
- the presence of raw materials for the process;
- good transport links that enable raw materials to be brought in easily and finished products to be distributed;
- people with the appropriate skills to work in the industry;
- access to essential services such as water and energy supplies;
- the effects the process may have on the environment in terms of, for example, chemical and noise pollution or increased traffic flow;
- costs of land on which to build the factory.

People who use science or scientific skills are not only found in large organisations. The large national or international companies are very well known and information about them is easy to find. You should remember that many people working with science are employed in much smaller local organisations, which can be easily overlooked and perhaps not even considered as users of science.

Many people who are not even considered as scientists use science in their work. For some of these people, science plays a major part in their work, for example **doctors**, **nurses**, **veterinary surgeons**, and **some types of engineers** and **architects**. **Photographers**, **farmers**, **gardeners** and **brewers** also use science in their work, but to a lesser extent.

7 Explain the difference between local, national and international organisations.

8 Briefly describe the scientific skills used by each of the workers listed in bold type on the right.

Figure 1.6 Many types of service use science.

2 Investigating organisations that use science

When completing your report for Unit 1 you will need to:
- identify and describe the types of scientific activity carried out;
- describe the importance of the activity to society or the community;
- put the employees into one of three classes: major, significant and small users of science.

The list below will help you in identifying organisations that use science and the type of activities they carry out.

The types of service that use science may include those that:

Figure 1.7 Science is used when making many products.

- provide education in science, for example schools, colleges and universities;
- provide and promote the health of individuals, for example general practitioners, dental surgeries, hospitals and public health laboratories;
- are involved in the energy distribution service, for example electricity and gas;
- provide communications systems, for example telephone, television and radio services and radar systems;
- provide animal welfare, for example veterinary practices;
- are involved in cosmetic care, for example hair salons.

Other types of business and organisation that use science may make or process products for sale. This type of organisation may:
- produce food and drink products, for example in-store bakeries at the supermarket;
- produce chemicals or products from chemicals, for example paints, fertilisers and plastics;
- produce electrical or electronic equipment, for example televisions, mobile phones and cookers;
- produce mechanical devices, for example lawn mowers or cars;
- extract or refine materials from natural resources, for example metals, cement or gravel.

2.1 Where do I find the information I need?

There are many sources of information you can use. Probably the best information is that which you collect yourself from local organisations. The best way of doing this is to prepare a questionnaire that will allow you to collect the information you need before making a visit.

Possible questions may include:
- what does the organisation make or do?
- why is it located here?
- how is science used?
- what skills do the employees have?
- what are the benefits for society of the products or services?
- does the organisation have any effects on the environment – and if so, how are they controlled?

Other places where information may be found include:
- the internet – large organisations publish useful information about the type of work they carry out, which may be easily accessed;
- your local careers service or Connexions advisor;
- local and national newspapers where job advertisements are sometimes placed;
- friends, family and neighbours, who may be employed in an organisation that uses science;
- using your work experience placement as a source of information.

9 Make a list of the organisations that use science in your area, and give a reason why each is located where it is.

10 Describe exactly what each organisation on your list produces or does.

3 Investigating the roles of scientists and those who use science

When completing your report for Unit 1 you will need to:
- identify the job titles and qualifications of the people who perform them;
- find out what skills are used by the people employed;
- find out what skills scientists need, in addition to their qualifications;
- find out what careers are available in science and science-related areas.

The types of scientific activity undertaken in the organisations you identify will vary. There are many types of job available in scientific or related organisations, ranging from research scientist to production manager; from laboratory technician to clerical assistant. The type of job will depend on the qualifications of the person. In addition, many organisations run their own training schemes, for example through Modern Apprenticeship or National Traineeship schemes, to help employees to gain further qualifications.

The Additional Applied Science course concentrates on the work of food scientists, forensic scientists and sports scientists. Here are three case studies to give you a flavour of the type of work these scientists may be involved in.

Case Study – The work of the food scientist

Food scientists are often responsible for developing new food products and improving existing ones, and for setting standards in producing, packaging and marketing food.

Some food scientists engage in basic research: discovering new food sources; analysing food content to determine levels of vitamins, fat, sugar or protein; or searching for substitutes for harmful additives. They also develop ways to process, preserve, package or store food (including baking, blanching, canning, drying, evaporation and pasteurisation).

Other food scientists enforce government regulations: inspecting food-processing areas and ensuring that sanitation, safety, quality and waste management standards are met. Food scientists may specialise in fields such as meat and dairy products, or seafood. They may also work in areas such as marketing and management, production supervision, quality control or research and development.

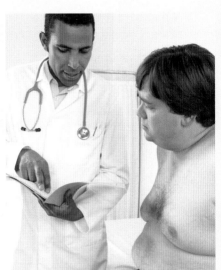

Figure 1.8 A dietician advising a patient on diet

It is also possible that food scientists may be trained as dieticians, and may be found working in hospitals advising people such as diabetics on a suitable diet.

Food scientists may be involved in the following types of work:
- making sure hygienic conditions, storage and procedures are maintained during the processing and packaging of food;
- testing and analysing both raw ingredients and processed foods for nutritional value and microbiological quality, and checking foods for colour, taste and flavour;
- developing new food products and devising methods to produce them;
- supervising the cleaning and maintenance of machinery used in food processing;
- comparing products with those of other brands, and participating in surveys that provide information to management about new products;
- supervising the transport of foodstuffs such as fruit, vegetables and milk, and inspecting for spoilage;
- developing quality control procedures for the manufacture of products in plants or factories;
- analysing results and experimental data.

Case Study – The work of the forensic scientist

Forensic scientists use scientific techniques to identify and match substances and objects. Most of the work completed by forensic scientists is done to help police investigate crimes, but forensic methods can also be used for other purposes, for example to study archaeological specimens; to investigate the cause of an industrial accident; or to show whether or not people are related. Many types of materials and objects need to be investigated, so a wide variety of scientific techniques are used. The results often have to be presented as evidence in a court of law, so accuracy and reliability are very important.

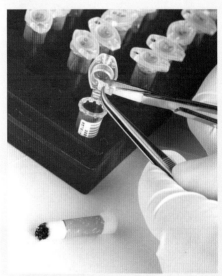

Figure 1.9 DNA testing for saliva traces to collect trace evidence

There are three main areas of forensic science, and other branches of science are often involved. The three main areas are:
- **Chemistry** – mainly crimes against property. This includes the analysis of contact traces such as glass and paint, also fire investigation and serial number restoration. Approximately 80% of cases involve drugs analyses.
- **Biology** – mainly crimes against the person. Violent crime makes up most of the case types encountered, and the majority of examinations involve blood and other body fluids; DNA testing is also used. The use of DNA testing is increasing rapidly following

the introduction of a nationwide DNA database. Crimes from many years ago are now being re-examined because of new DNA evidence. This area of forensic science also includes the analysis of hairs and fibres.

- **Drugs and toxicology** – drink- and drug-driving cases, and the criminal and non-criminal investigation of deaths due to overdoses, poisons and drugs.

A forensic scientist may be involved in the following:
- recording findings and collecting trace evidence from scenes of crime or accidents;
- analysing samples such as hair, body fluids (such as blood or saliva), glass, paint and drugs in the laboratory;
- applying various techniques, for example DNA profiling, mass spectrometry and chromatography, and presenting written and verbal evidence in court that may be cross-examined.

Case Study – The work of the sports scientist

Sports scientists help people to improve their sporting performance or their general health. They apply expert knowledge gained in scientific fields such as medicine, physiology, biomechanics (the study of human movement), nutrition, psychology, physiotherapy/massage and performance analysis.

Figure 1.10 A sports trainer working in a gym

While sports scientists may not have specialised in all these areas, they may have trained as a dietician, medical practitioner, sports trainer or physiotherapist, for example. Sports scientists often attend training sessions and sporting fixtures to monitor sporting performances, as well as working in an office or testing laboratory. They have a high level of contact with the public and good communication skills.

A sports scientist may be involved in the following:
- devising treatment and exercise programmes to assist people to return to training or competition;
- designing, or assisting in designing, training programmes for people to improve their sporting performance without causing injury, or to strengthen particular areas of the body;
- referring clients to other specialists such as orthopaedic surgeons, rheumatologists and physiotherapists.

Figure 1.11 Food scientists work with plant breeders and growers to produce food efficiently and safely.

Figure 1.12 Sports and materials scientists work to produce modern lightweight clothing for athletes and swimmers.

3.1 Finding out about the skills and qualifications needed by scientists

While completing the work for Unit 1 of the Additional Applied Science course, you will find out about the knowledge and skills needed by some other types of scientist. Some examples are listed below, together with examples of those who may not be called scientists, but use scientific skills:
- healthcare, including doctors, nurses, physiotherapists, surgeons, dentists, opticians, radiographers, midwives, laboratory technicians;
- hairdressers and beauticians;
- engineers, including electrical, electronic, mechanical and information technology;
- research scientists, including chemists, biologists and physicists;
- media and communication, including those working with photography, mobile phones and digital media;
- education, including teachers, lecturers and technicians;
- plant breeders and growers in horticulture and agriculture;
- veterinary care, including surgeons, nurses, radiographers and laboratory technicians;
- weather forecasters;
- energy consultants, including those who work for the electricity and gas service industries, advising on home energy consumption;
- geologists and those working to monitor and improve the environment;
- transport, including car and aircraft maintenance and design;
- pharmacists and dispensing chemists;
- clothing, including production of man-made fibres and dyes.

It is necessary for you to appreciate the skills that may be used by scientists. You will be using many of these skills during your course. Scientists and those who use science not only make things, but also may have to:

- plan carefully how to carry out an activity;
- research in laboratories or from books, the internet or perhaps by undertaking a survey;
- record the results of their activities accurately;
- observe what happens during, for example, chemical reactions or biological investigations, using the naked eye and instruments such as microscopes;
- make measurements of, for example, mass, volume, temperature or distance;
- use specific scientific knowledge, for example doctors, nurses and dentists;
- communicate with other people;
- use numeracy skills;
- use a computer and particular software packages;
- use practical skills, for example telephone engineers, surgeons or chefs.

Figure 1.13 Scientists at work

⑪ Do the following for the organisations you identified in questions 9 and 10.
  a) Classify them as local, national or international.
  b) Give the job titles of those employees who use science.
  c) Find out each of these people's qualifications.
  d) Make a list of the skills used by those who work in the organisations.

When investigating the roles and skills of people employed by organisations, you will need to plan the type of information you want to find out. The following questions will help you:

- what is the title of the job?
- what specific scientific skills are needed to carry out the job?
- what other types of skill are needed for the job?
- are there particular health and safety issues associated with the job?
- what particular qualifications are needed for the job?

You may be able to obtain a job description as part of your investigation, which will give many of the answers to your questions.

4 Health and safety in scientific workplaces

When completing work on science in the workplace, you also need to find out about:

- health and safety checks in the workplace;
- risk assessments for activities performed in the workplace;
- what can be done to prevent accidents from hazards in a scientific workplace;
- emergency procedures followed if an accident is caused by these hazards.

While investigating scientific organisations, you will need also to investigate some aspects of health and safety – this will help you when completing the next section of Unit 1.

Those who work with science are very aware of the hazards and risks involved and, as a result, have one of the best safety records compared with other types of work.

Unfortunately accidents do happen – in the home, on the road, on the games field and in the workplace. Scientists are very aware of the potential dangers involved in some of the work they do, and take appropriate precautions to prevent accidents. The news item below illustrates the type of accident that can happen and shows that the very best plans can sometimes go wrong.

Explosion causes plastics factory to close

A plastics factory was partially destroyed yesterday by an explosion. The explosion took place during maintenance work following the discovery of an electrical fault in part of the process machinery that produces fibre for the clothing industry.

An air ambulance was called and took one employee to a specialist burns unit and several others were treated at the scene for shock. Black plumes of smoke could be seen rising into the air up to 5 miles away from the incident.

The owners of the factory said that the Health and Safety Executive would conduct a full enquiry into the incident and that the factory would remain closed at least for the next few days while the investigation took place.

⑫ Suggest some possible reasons for the explosion.

Incidents such as this are very rare because of the care taken and the many safety precautions required in workplaces.

The Heath and Safety at Work Act 1974 governs safety in workplaces. From this act, there come strict regulations which control the way scientists (and **all other workers** in the UK) work. If you go on work placement schemes from school, you will be subject to these regulations and you can be sacked for the blatant disregard of the safety rules within the place of work, e.g. refusing to wear eye protection. The Act also applies to the school you are in at the moment.

Strict regulations control the way in which scientists work and behave in laboratories and other workplaces. It is important for you to be aware of some of these and to understand their purpose.

Regulations are designed to protect the people who work in potentially hazardous environments. All places of employment are responsible for ensuring these regulations are followed.

Some examples are given below.

4.1 The Management of Health and Safety at Work Regulations

These regulations ensure that employers provide their employees with a healthy and safe place in which to work. In particular, employers are responsible for:
- making arrangements for implementing the health and safety measures identified as necessary by a risk assessment (see page 22) for any task undertaken;
- appointing competent people to ensure health safety procedures are carried out;
- setting up emergency procedures and ensuring employees know what to do, for example in the case of fire;
- providing clear information and training to employees.

4.2 Control of Substances Hazardous to Health (COSHH) Regulations

COSHH Regulations apply to the storage and use of all substances that are hazardous, for example:
- substances that are toxic, harmful, corrosive or cause irritation;
- substances that may cause cancer or birth defects;
- microorganisms that may cause disease;
- substances that have workplace exposure limits, such as harmful solvents and gases;
- dust in large concentrations.

Figure 1.14 The Health and Safety Executive enforces safety regulations.

COSHH Regulations apply to all types of workplace, including schools and colleges (not just science but design and technology, art, pottery, etc.). They also affect many other functions in running a school, including cleaning, any maintenance work involving chemicals (paints, glues, etc.), maintenance of swimming pools, and pesticide spraying.

4.3 Electricity at Work Regulations (portable appliance testing)

Nearly a quarter of all electrical accidents involve portable equipment. Some of these accidents result in fire, but most cause electric shock. Portable equipment includes any appliance that is connected to the mains by a cable and plug. The law demands that this equipment is tested regularly. (You may have noticed labels attached to the equipment in your school stating when the last test was carried out.) The test will detect problems such as a broken earth wire, faulty insulation or use of incorrect fuse.

4.4 Investigating health and safety in organisations

When planning to investigate health and safety in organisations, the following questions will help you:
- what are the particular health and safety concerns associated with the type of work carried out by the organisation?
- who is responsible for health and safety?
- what sort of health and safety checks are carried out?
- what happens if an accident occurs?

You might be able to obtain a copy of a risk assessment and accident report form used by the organisation.

You should also look for warning signs and notices, and compare these with any you may have seen in your school or college.

Page 16 contains an example of typical risk assessment and accident report forms, similar to those you may find in the workplace.

⓭ For one of your identified organisations, do the following.
  a) Make a list of the health and safety notices or signs you saw when you visited the organisation (Topic 1 of Chapter 2 may help you).
  b) Find out about the particular health and safety issues connected with making the product or providing the service.
  c) Find out about the procedures for reporting an accident.
  d) Find out who is responsible for health and safety.

Risk assessment form:

Name and status of the assessor:
Date:
Activity being assessed:
Known or expected hazards associated with the activity:
The risk of injury and its severity likely to arise from these hazards:
Who is at risk?
Measure to be taken to reduce the level of risk:
Training requirements:
Emergency action:
Signature of assessor: **Revision date:**

Accident report form:

Site where incident/accident took place:
Name of person in charge of site:
Name of injured person:
Address of injured person:
Date and time of incident/accident:
Nature of incident/accident:
Give details of how and precisely where the incident/accident took place:
Give full details of the action taken including any First Aid treatment and the name(s) of the First Aider(s):
Were any of the following contacted?   **Police:**   Yes ☐   No ☐   **Parent/carer:**   Yes ☐   No ☐   **Ambulance:**   Yes ☐   No ☐   **Wife/husband:**   Yes ☐   No ☐
Signed: **Date:**

Chapter 2
Working safely in science

Chapter 2 is divided into three topics:

1 Hazards and risks in the laboratory
2 First Aid in the laboratory
3 Prevention of fire in the laboratory

In this section of Unit 1 you need to produce a report of an investigation carried out into working safely in a scientific workplace, and a comparison with the health and safety in your school or college.

Your teacher will assess this section of the course as part of your coursework. While completing your report, you will need to use the statements at the beginning of each topic as a guide to the information you should include. You will also need to use the Unit 1 assessment grid in the AQA Additional Applied Science specification. The assessment grid is divided into three stages. The checklist below details what should be included at each stage.

To reach a maximum mark at Stage one, your work on safety in the school or college laboratory should include sections on hazards and risks, First Aid and fire. You may wish to concentrate on one of these sections more than the others. Your work should also explain why risk assessments are important when working in the laboratory.

To obtain even better marks, you should investigate the health and safety issues in a workplace that uses science or scientific skills. Your investigation should be presented under the same headings as you used for the school or college investigation.

To gain the best marks, you should compare the two investigations and comment, with examples, on the similarities and differences in the school or college compared with the workplace. For example, there may be differences in the way risk assessments are prepared and presented, and in how accidents are reported. There will be similarities in the types of signs and symbols you observe, although these may not necessarily be for the same hazards.

Figure 2.1 Working safely in a laboratory

1 Hazards and risks in the laboratory

When completing your report for this section of Unit 1 you will need to:
- identify hazard warning signs;
- identify biological, chemical and physical hazards, including radioactive substances, and their associated risks;
- know about health and safety procedures;
- understand the use of risk assessments;
- know about the safety measures employed for handling radioactive materials and the procedures adopted to ensure that people who work with these materials are not exposed to unacceptable risk;
- know about how unwanted or waste materials, including radioactive substances, are disposed of safely.

Regulations such as those described in Chapter 1 (pages 14–15) will not guarantee the safety of those working in a school or college laboratory or other scientific workplace. It is important that you take responsibility for your own actions and behaviour. You must learn to use all equipment properly and safely, and follow the correct procedure. If you are unsure how to use a particular piece of equipment or carry out an experiment, you should always ask. Like many other workplaces, your school or college will have rules and regulations that must be followed when working in the laboratory.

> **①** What are your school laboratory rules?

Here is a list of laboratory rules found in a college science laboratory.
- Eye protection should be worn at all times.
- No eating, drinking or smoking in laboratories.
- Laboratory coats must he worn when handling corrosive, toxic or flammable materials.
- Gloves should be worn when necessary, especially when handling corrosive and highly toxic materials.
- Never work alone.
- Do not pipette by mouth.
- If you see a colleague doing something dangerous, point it out to him or her and make sure the supervisor or teacher is informed.

- Know where safety equipment (eyewash, shower, extinguishers) is located and how to use it.
- Know how to clean up spills of the chemicals you use.
- Wash your hands after handling chemicals and before leaving the laboratory.
- Do not wear open shoes.
- Bare legs are not acceptable when handling hot, cold or sharp materials as well as toxic or corrosive chemicals.

> ❷ Compare your list of laboratory rules with the one above and comment on any differences.

Health and safety regulations may seem long and complicated and, together with the rules in your school or college, difficult to remember. Rules and regulations are based on common sense and sensible behaviour. When working in the laboratory, you should take time to think about what you are doing and be aware of those around you. It may seem that laboratories are very dangerous places in which to work. The purpose of rules and regulations is to minimise the risks – it is because scientists are very aware of the dangers involved that laboratories are among the safest places in which to work.

The theme behind all these rules and regulations is the same:

STOP, PLAN and THINK before you start.

Safety

Always wear safety spectacles and always keep your workspace clear.

Think safety

Hazard
The potential to cause harm or damage

Risk
The likelihood of a hazard causing harm in practice

1.1 Hazards and risks

You need to appreciate the difference between hazard and risk.
- A **hazard** is the potential that a particular activity, substance, or piece of equipment has to do harm.
- **Risk** is the likelihood or chance that a hazard will cause harm or damage in practice.

During this course you will be using substances and equipment that are hazardous. You will be expected to be able to recognise chemical, biological and physical hazards involved in completing your laboratory work.

1.2 Working with chemicals

Chemical hazards are identified by symbols that have definite meanings. These symbols are universally recognised throughout the world and have very specific meanings.

Corrosive

A substance that may destroy living tissues on contact with the tissue

Highly flammable

A substance that catches fire easily

Explosive

A chemical that may explode

Irritant

A substance that may cause irritation to the skin

Harmful

A substance that may cause damage to health

Toxic

A substance that, at low levels, can cause damage to health

Dangerous for the environment

A substance that may present an immediate or delayed danger to the environment

Oxidising

A substance that provides oxygen, allowing other materials to burn more fiercely

Safety

Biohazard
Risk of infection or
contamination

1.3 Working with microorganisms

In biology laboratories where microorganisms are being used, there is always a danger from infection and contamination by bacteria or viruses. Suitable precautions must be taken to ensure all specimens are neutralised and disposed of correctly. Microorganisms that are used for experiments should always be stored away from areas where food or drink is consumed, prepared or eaten.

In school and college laboratories, only certain types of microorganism may be used. Following any experiments, you will be given clear instructions on the procedure to follow, and the material will be carefully neutralised and disposed of for you.

One of the better known hazards arising from the handling of human biological material is HIV (human immunodeficiency virus). Its ease of transfer has made everyone more aware of the need for care when handling any type of material that has the potential to cause infection.

Safety

Radiation
Risk of radioactive
emission

1.4 Working with radioactive material

You will not be required to use radioactive material during your course, but you will be able to see sources being used by your teacher. You should be aware of the dangers and the safety measures used when handling this type of material.

Material that emits radiation can damage living cells. The more cells damaged, the greater is the danger to the body. The amount of damage done depends on both the intensity and type of radiation.

Gamma radiation is so penetrating that it will pass through the body without much harm, provided the amount is small. Beta radiation is not so penetrating, therefore more is absorbed by human cells, making it more dangerous. Alpha radiation is even less penetrating and, if allowed into the body, can cause severe damage. However, because of the low penetrating effect of alpha radiation, the layer of dead cells forming the outer surface of our skin normally stops it. Alpha radiation is obviously very harmful if inhaled, as there is no outer surface of skin to protect internal organs.

Radioactive sources used in school laboratories have a low intensity, but nevertheless should be treated with respect. They are handled with forceps and not allowed near the face, and more especially the eyes, and should always be kept in an approved storage cabinet. In industry, radioactive sources are handled using much longer tongs and transported in thick, lead-lined containers. Lead and concrete walls are often used to protect people who work in industry with radioactive sources.

Radioactive sources are hazardous only if handled incorrectly, and are used for a number of purposes in the scientific workplace, such as:

- food irradiation – to kill infesting insects or prevent potatoes sprouting;
- medical uses – for killing cancer cells or monitoring bone growth;
- leak tracing – in pipework that may be inaccessible;
- thickness gauging – for thin sheets of, for example, paper or aluminium foil during manufacture.

1.5 Working with gas and electricity

Safety

Electrical hazard
Risk of electrical shock

Many laboratory activities involve working with either gas or electricity. In the workplace, only certain trained people are allowed to replace electrical plugs or fuses (Electricity at Work Regulations, page 15). When using electrical appliances in any situation, the same good practice should apply:

- be careful not to spill water or any other type of liquid near an electrical appliance;
- before using, make sure there are no loose wires visible;
- check visually for any other obvious damage;
- take care not to allow loose wires or cable to trail across floors or benches.

The Bunsen burner is taken for granted in most laboratories, but is frequently used without much thought. When using the Bunsen burner you should remember to:

- check that all flammable liquids are securely stoppered and preferably put away in a flameproof store;
- check that the air hole is shut before lighting the burner;
- have a lighter ready before turning on the gas;
- leave a visible flame (yellow) burning whenever the burner is not actually heating – preferably it should be turned off;
- check that the tubing is not caught around other apparatus in your working area;
- arrange your working area so that you do not have to lean over the lighted burner at any time.

1.6 Using your knowledge of hazards to ensure safer working

Risk assessment
A detailed assessment of the hazards and associated risks, together with control measures

Before starting any activity in the laboratory, you should compile a **risk assessment**. Your risk assessment should identify the hazards associated with the substance, organism or equipment being used for a particular task, and assess the risks associated with them. The risk assessment should also contain details of how these risks may be controlled or prevented.

Your risk assessment will probably look different from the one that appears on page 16. Your risk assessment must include all the substances and equipment used during any one practical activity. Your teacher may give you a blank risk assessment form to complete. You should learn to research the hazards and associated risks yourself – the more independently you work, the higher your marks will be. Your teacher will help you by suggesting the places for you to look. The risk assessment form may look similar to the example below.

Risk assessment

Name:	Date:	Practical activity	
Substance/equipment	Hazard	Risk	Control measure

A risk assessment should be completed for every practical activity and should consider:

1 The hazardous substance or substances being used or made, and risks associated with them, for example:
   - problems that might arise from exposure to the substance;
   - how a person might be harmed by the substance (swallowing, inhaling or absorbing through the skin);
   - particular people who may be harmed (working as a group, in pairs, on your own, etc.).

2 The precautions that may be taken to minimise the risks, for example:
   - find an alternative substance, or use smaller quantities;
   - find an alternative method that limits exposure to the substance, if possible;
   - use a fume cupboard if necessary;
   - isolate your working area if necessary.

3 Any other risks, including:
   - risks from other equipment (e.g. electrical);
   - risks arising from the environment in which you are working.

Details of hazards associated with particular substances may be obtained from information found in your school or college science department.

Information is published by:

CLEAPSS (Consortium of Local Education Authorities for the Provision of Science Services)
www.cleapss.org.uk

SSERC (Scottish Schools Equipment Research Centre)
www.sserc.org.uk

ASE (The Association for Science Education)
www.ase.org.uk

3 Explain the difference between a hazard and a risk.

4 Give an example of a hazardous chemical and describe how you would reduce the risks when using it.

Safety

REMEMBER
Always report accidents.
Always ask for help if you are not sure what to do.

5 Why is it important to take notes of any actions taken or conversations at the scene of an accident?

1.7 What you should do in case of an accident

The most important thing to do if an accident happens is to tell someone – even if the accident does not seem serious. Students working in the school or college laboratory, or employees working in the workplace, might think it is better to keep quiet because the incident seemed very minor. A simple liquid spill in the chemistry laboratory is easily wiped up – but just suppose there was some left and the liquid was hazardous in some way, such as an acid. Someone else may be hurt inadvertently as a result of what seemed like a minor incident.

In the case of major accidents, the law is that these must be reported. The Health and Safety Executive may want to investigate and a report of the accident will always be made. In certain circumstances the scene of the accident may well be preserved (left untouched) to enable a full investigation to be made. Your school or college is just the same as all other workplaces and will have a procedure for reporting accidents.

Here is a typical checklist of things to do and record if an accident does happen, and you are involved or witness the accident.

Accident report checklist:

1 **General information**
   - Class, activity or event in which accident occurred.
   - Date and time of accident.
   - Person in charge.
   - Any person injured.
   - Any witnesses.

2 **Accident information**
   - Location of accident.
   - What was the injured doing? (Just the **facts**, do not include opinions or a determination of the cause.)
   - Safety steps that were actually taken.

3 **First Aid or medical assistance**
   - What type of injury? (Just facts about general nature of injury.)
   - What emergency care was given?
   - Was the injured taken to the hospital? If so, how was the injured taken to hospital?
   - Who did what?

4 **Follow-up**
   - Take notes of any conversations with the injured, or their family and friends.
   - Inform the teacher or lecturer.
   - **Do not** take immediate steps to make changes without the advice of a supervisor.
   - Save any possible evidence.

2 First Aid in the laboratory

When completing your report for this section of Unit 1 you will need to know:

- the basic First Aid to give in the case of some common laboratory accidents;
- the situations in which it would be dangerous to give First Aid;
- why it is useful to have a First Aid qualification;
- the names of organisations that give training for First Aid qualifications and how to contact them.

When an accident happens in the workplace, it is important that the people who may be close to the scene of the accident know what to do. Your school or college, like other workplaces, will have people who are trained in giving First Aid treatment if an accident occurs. They may have received their training and gained qualifications from one of the three voluntary organisations that run training courses in First Aid. You should be aware of these organisations and know how to contact them. They are:

St. John Ambulance
www.sja.org.uk

British Red Cross
www.redcross.org.uk/firstaid

St. Andrew's Ambulance Association
www.firstaid.org.uk

> ❻ Use the Yellow Pages to find the address of your local branch of these organisations.
>
> ❼ Find out about the qualifications you could obtain in First Aid.

2.1 What is First Aid?

First Aid is the first treatment given to a person for any injury. The person nearby the incident should apply immediate remedial measures, before the arrival of a qualified expert. In giving this treatment, your responsibility is to help recovery and prevent the condition from becoming more serious.

2.2 Emergency scene management

> **Emergency scene management**
> The management of an accident site

Before trying to deal with any situation requiring First Aid, you must assess the situation carefully. **Emergency scene management** is the sequence of actions you should follow at the scene of an emergency to ensure that safe and appropriate First Aid is given. If first on the scene, you should take the following steps.

1 Take charge of the situation.
2 Call for help. Other people on the scene may be more qualified than you to deal with the situation – if not, ask them for help in assisting with treatment or seeking further assistance. If in school or college, they may be sent to fetch a teacher or a health and safety officer.
3 Assess hazards – make the area safe. It is important to assess if you are in any danger as well as the casualty. It is crucial that you minimise the danger to yourself and guard against further casualties. This is particularly important in some of the examples given later. For instance, in the case of gas leaks the source should be cut off, if possible. Electricity should be switched off in the case of electric shock. Your own safety is important – you have to treat the casualty without yourself becoming a casualty.
4 Determine what happened and the type of injury sustained. You may have to contribute to the accident report form later and give details of the actions you have taken.

2.3 Common laboratory accidents

Some accidents that occur in laboratories include:
- heat burns and scalds;
- chemical burns;
- injury caused by breathing in fumes or swallowing chemicals;
- electric shock;
- cuts and damage to the eyes from particles or chemicals.

It is important that you understand what to do if any these types of accident occur, in addition to informing the person in charge. Here are some guidelines for the treatment of these laboratory accidents.

Heat burns and scalds

Accidental contact with hot objects frequently causes burns and scalds. In the treatment of heat burns and scalds, the aim is to reduce the effect of heat on the affected area, prevent any infection from entering, and relieve pain. In order to achieve these aims you should do the following.

- Cool the burn right away – immerse the burned area in cold water; or pour cold water on the area; or cover it with a clean, wet cloth until the pain has lessened.
- Loosen or remove anything on the burned area that is tight, such as jewellery or tight clothing, before swelling begins.
- Do not remove anything that is stuck to the burned area.
- When the pain has lessened, loosely cover the burn with a clean, non-fluffy dressing. If the burned area is large, use a sheet. Secure the dressing with tape, making sure there is no tape on the burned area.
- Arrange for medical help.

<table><tr><td>**Safety**</td></tr><tr><td>REMEMBER
Use your common sense.
Do not attempt to do too much.
Know your own limitations.
Always seek help.</td></tr></table>

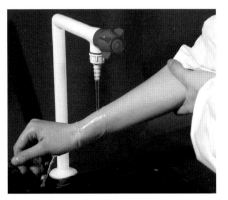

Figure 2.2 Cool burns straight away.

<table><tr><td>**Safety**</td></tr><tr><td>Do not break blisters or move any loose skin.
Do not use adhesive dressings.</td></tr></table>

8 What is the purpose of the cold water in treating burns?

9 Why should you not break the blisters when treating burns?

10 Why should you not remove anything that is stuck to the burned area?

Chemical burns

Many substances that you use in the laboratory are irritating to the skin and may harm tissue, even after a short contact time. Common substances found in the home, such as bleaches, household cleaners and paint stripper, may also cause chemical burns. The first sign of a chemical burn is usually when the casualty complains that the skin is stinging or feeling hot. The skin will often appear red. The aim of any treatment is to identify and remove the harmful chemical as quickly as possible. In order to achieve these aims you should do the following.

- Flush the affected area with cool running water for at least 10–15 minutes.
- Remove all clothing and jewellery that has been contaminated.
- Monitor the casualty for shock, and seek medical assistance.

Injury caused by breathing in fumes or swallowing

Many people may come into contact with potentially dangerous chemicals or gases as a result of the type of work they do. Workplaces using dangerous gases are required to display notices that indicate any action to be taken in case of accidents. Anyone suffering from the effects of gas or toxic fumes needs air – the area should be well ventilated and medical assistance should be requested.

In cases where chemicals have been swallowed, it is important that the substance is identified if possible, and medical help requested. You should never give anything by mouth unless specifically instructed to do so by a medical officer or someone in authority.

Electric shock

Laboratories, workshops, homes, offices and shops all have electrical appliances that can cause electrical injuries if they develop a fault or are not used correctly. Water, in particular, is a good conductor of electricity – using electrical equipment with wet hands or while standing on a wet floor can often cause electrical injury. Electric shock or injury is caused when an electric current passes through the body. Before helping a person who has suffered an electric shock, it is important to make sure the person is no longer in contact with the

> ⓫ Why is it important not to touch the casualty until the electricity is switched off?

source of electricity. You should always first switch off the mains supply and then remove the plug from the socket.

Electricity may cause burns to the body at the point of contact and these should be treated as a normal burn. The person may also become unconscious and suffer from shock – in all such cases further medical help should be sought.

Cuts and damage to the eyes from particles or chemicals

Any eye injury can be dangerous as particles may perforate the eyeball, resulting in internal damage and possible infection. The most common problems, other than loose eyelashes, are caused by small particles of dust and grit. You should not attempt to remove any particle if it is on the coloured part of the eye or embedded in the eye.

Normally a person with a particle in their eye will complain of some pain or itchiness of the eye. The eye will often become red, and water intensely. The vision may also be affected. In treating the eye to remove any particle you should take great care and seek immediate help if unsuccessful.

If a particle is embedded in the eye you should do the following.

- Do **not** remove the particle.
- Cover **both** eyes with sterile dressings to immobilise them – this will minimise movement of the injured eye.
- Do **not** rub, or apply pressure or ice to the eye. (If the injury is a black eye, you may apply ice to the cheek and the area around the eye, but not directly on the eyeball itself.)

> ⓬ Why is it important to remove contact lenses after flushing the eye?
>
> ⓭ Find out who is responsible for First Aid in your school or college and what qualifications they have.

If the particle is not embedded, it may be removed by flushing the eye with a sterile eyewash solution.

To flush the eye you should do the following.

- If the chemical particle or foreign body is in only one eye, flush by positioning the casualty's head to the side with the contaminated eye downwards to prevent flushing any chemical from one eye to another.
- Flush with a sterile eyewash solution. If this is not available then tap water should be used.
- Remove contact lenses after flushing.

3 Prevention of fire in the laboratory

When completing your report for this section of Unit 1 you will need to describe:
- what must be done if you hear a fire alarm or smoke alarm;
- what must be done if you find a fire;
- how fire doors function;
- why different types of fire extinguisher (water, carbon dioxide, dry powder, foam, fire blanket) are used on different types of fire;
- the use of automatic sprinkler systems.

Fire is one of the major hazards in scientific workplaces, particularly in chemistry laboratories and industries that use chemicals. In 2003 the total number of fires reported in the United Kingdom was 621 000.

3.1 Causes of fire

For a fire to start, three things are needed:
- fuel;
- oxygen;
- a source of heat.

If any one of these is missing, a fire cannot start. Taking steps to avoid the three coming together will reduce the chances of a fire occurring.

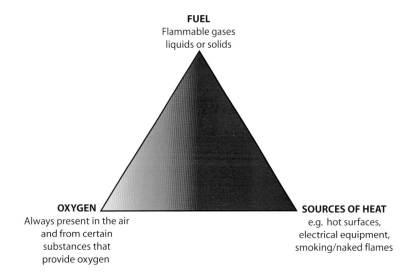

Figure 2.3 The fire triangle

Figure 2.4 Fire crews fighting a large industrial fire.

Fire-fighting involves the removal of at least one of the components of the fire triangle. However, fires are best fought by prevention. Some sort of human error – for example incorrect decisions being taken, or the failure to follow instructions – causes most fires. Many fires could be prevented if we were alert and careful at all times.

In the laboratory and scientific workplace, fires may be caused in a number of ways. It is important that you are aware of the possible sources of fire.

Table 2.1 shows some of the possible sources of fire in a laboratory.

Chemicals	Many chemicals will easily catch fire and must be stored under the correct conditions. Chemicals must also be used correctly – many should not be used near a naked flame in case they catch fire or explode. You should always check before using any chemical
Laboratory burners and open flames	Fire may be caused by, for example, Bunsen burners being placed too close to where people are working or too close to other combustible materials
Hot surfaces	Combustible materials may catch fire if placed on, or too close to, hot surfaces
Static electricity	Static electricity can produce sparks that may start a fire
Electrical equipment	Fires may occur if electrical equipment or machinery is allowed to overheat and is not ventilated correctly

Table 2.1 Causes of fire in a laboratory

A major cause of fire spreading in the workplace or laboratory is poor housekeeping – for example not clearing up spillages, scraps of paper and other materials, which can easily ignite if allowed too near a flame.

3.2 Dealing with fire

It is important that you know what to do if you discover a fire, or hear a fire alarm or smoke alarm. Look for the instructions in your laboratory and learn them.

Typical notices may contain information like that given below.

If you discover a fire you should do the following.

Figure 2.5 Remove unnecessary items from laboratory workspaces

Safety

Always keep your workplace clean and free of rubbish.

- Raise the alarm immediately.
- If you are carrying out an experiment, make sure your work area is safe by turning off all heat sources.
- Assess the situation from a safe distance.
- If the fire is small and you are able to tackle it, make one attempt with an appropriate fire extinguisher or fire blanket.
- Leave the room as quickly as possible, making sure all other people have left.

If you hear a fire alarm you should do the following.

- Raise the alarm immediately.
- If you are carrying out an experiment, make sure your work area is safe by turning off all heat sources.
- Close all doors and windows.
- Quickly and quietly evacuate the building via the nearest exit.
- Assemble in the area that has been assigned for your group.

If there is a fire, the main priority is to ensure that everyone reaches a place of safety quickly. It is important that you know where to go if a fire does occur. Putting the fire out is less important than reaching a place of safety – the greatest danger from fire in any workplace is its spread as well as the spread of heat and smoke. If a workplace does not have an adequate means of detection and giving warning or means of escape, a fire can trap people or they may be overcome by the heat and smoke before they can leave the building.

⓮ Why is it important to turn off all heat sources?

⓯ Why should you make sure all windows and doors are closed?

⓰ Why is it important that you assemble in the area assigned for your group?

Safety

Fire action

1. Operate nearest fire alarm.
2. Leave building by the nearest exit.
3. Report to the assembly point.

1. DO NOT stop to collect personal belongings.
2. DO NOT re-enter until told it is safe to do so.

Safety

When working in laboratories, you should always know where the safety equipment is located and how to raise the alarm.

Safety

You should use a fire extinguisher only if you feel confident to do so.

Fire extinguishers

There are four main kinds of fire extinguisher. You should be able to recognise the different types.

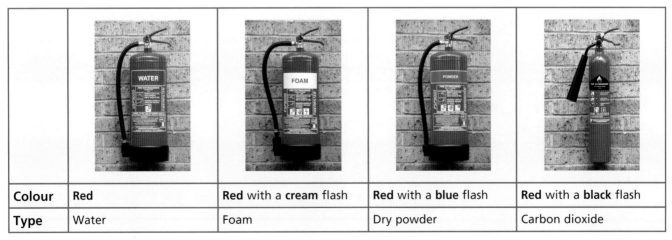

Colour	Red	Red with a **cream** flash	Red with a **blue** flash	Red with a **black** flash
Type	Water	Foam	Dry powder	Carbon dioxide

Table 2.2 Different types of fire extinguisher

Different types of fire extinguisher are used for different purposes. Table 2.3 summarises where each is mainly used. Fire extinguishers work by either starving the fire of oxygen, or cooling the fire down.

Extinguisher	Type of fire	Safety
Water	Wood, cloth, paper, plastics Fires involving solids	**Do not use water on burning fat or oil, or on electrical appliances**
Foam	Wood, cloth, paper, plastics Fires involving solids Liquids such as grease, fats, oil, paint and petrol	**Do not use on chip- or fat-pan fires**
Dry powder	Liquids such as grease, fats, oil, paint, petrol, etc.	You can use dry powder on live electrical equipment, but it does not penetrate the spaces in equipment easily and the fire may re-ignite This type of extinguisher does not cool the fire very well and you should take care that the fire does not re-ignite **Do not use on chip- or fat-pan fires**
Carbon dioxide	Liquids such as grease, fats, oil paint, petrol, etc.	This type of extinguisher does not cool the fire very well and you need to watch that the fire does not start up again Fumes from CO_2 extinguishers can be harmful if used in confined spaces: you should ventilate the area as soon as the fire has been controlled **Do not use on chip- or fat-pan fires**

Table 2.3 Types of fire extinguisher, their uses and precautions

Fire blankets

Fire blankets are made from a special material that does not burn. You can use a fire blanket to remove the oxygen supply and smother a fire – they are particularly good for putting out chip-pan fires and clothing on fire. It is important that you completely cover the fire when using a fire blanket, otherwise the fire will not be put out.

Figure 2.6 Fire blanket being opened

⑰ Explain why you should never put water on an electrical fire.

⑱ Explain why the use of a fire blanket is the recommended method for dealing with a chip-pan fire.

Figure 2.7 Fire doors being tested: the glass used is heated to over 920 °C for 1 hour – the glass should not break or allow heat to pass through.

Safety

Keep clear. Exit for escape route.

Use of fire doors to prevent the spread of fire

It is very likely that the door you use to enter and leave your laboratory is a fire door. Fire doors are typically made of steel or solid wood and are provided with specially tested components for opening and shutting, as well as wired, fire-rated glass windows. These doors protect the opening created in the 'fire wall' that separates the laboratory environment from the corridor. But they can only perform their job when used and maintained properly. Some fire doors are found in corridors and will shut automatically when the fire alarm sounds, making a fire wall and preventing fire from sweeping down the corridor.

Fire doors should always be used properly and never abused. The following rules should always be observed.

- Keep the door closed at all times, particularly when the laboratory is not occupied. The simple action of closing a fire door will help contain the products of a fire (heat and smoke) within the laboratory, while protecting other areas and the exit route.
- Never prop open the fire door with wedges or by bending the closing mechanism. Aside from possibly rendering the fire door inoperable due to physical damage, propping open fire doors will allow products of a fire to move into other areas and contribute to the spread and intensity of the fire.
- Never store equipment, bags or clothing against the fire door. Placing items of equipment in front of a fire door may result in these materials igniting if a fire breaks out on the other side of the door. This could create hazardous conditions in the corridor, not only for those exiting the building, but also for fire and other emergency teams entering the building to extinguish the fire.
- You should not nail or screw signs or other items to the fire door. Creating holes or cracks in a fire door will mean it is no longer secure against fire. Signs may be attached to fire doors, provided they are small (less than 5% of the area of the door) and attached with adhesive (to areas other than a wired-glass view panel).

Use of automatic sprinkler systems

Sprinkler systems are very effective in preventing the spread of fire. They are very common in workplaces and other public buildings. Recently, automatic sprinkler systems have also been designed for use in the home. Losses from fires in buildings that are protected by automatic sprinkler systems are estimated to be *one-tenth* of the losses in unprotected buildings.

In buildings fully protected by automatic sprinkler systems, it has been estimated that over a 10-year period:
- 99% of fires were controlled by sprinklers alone;
- 60% of fires were controlled by the spray from no more than four sprinklers.

Figure 2.8 A sprinkler head similar to those found in many large buildings

How sprinkler systems work

Automatic fire sprinklers are individually heat-activated and tied into a network of pipes that contain water under pressure. When the heat of a fire raises the sprinkler temperature to its operating point (usually around 65 °C), a solder link will melt or a liquid-filled glass bulb will shatter to open a single sprinkler, releasing water directly over the source of heat.

An automatic sprinkler system does not rely on human factors, such as familiarity with escape routes or emergency assistance. They work immediately to reduce the danger. Sprinklers will prevent fires from developing quickly and spreading throughout a building.

One major advantage of a sprinkler system is in the amount of water used and the damage it causes. Quick-response sprinklers release between 65 and 120 litres of water per minute, compared with 625 litres per minute released by a fire hose. The use of less water makes clearing up after a fire much easier.

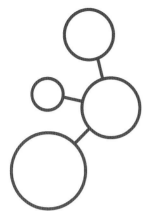

Unit 2
Science at work

Unit 3
Using scientific skills

In the AQA Additional Applied Science course Units 2 and 3 are divided into three sections covering food, forensic and sports science. Chapters 3, 4 and 5 contain material that you will need for both Units 2 and 3.

Chapter 3	Food science
Chapter 4	Forensic science
Chapter 5	Sports science

In these chapters, you will learn about the knowledge needed by food, forensic and sports scientists.

The **Unit 2** examination will be based on this knowledge.

You will also learn about some of the practical techniques that these scientists use.

In **Unit 3**, you will be given the opportunity to use some of these skills in your own food, forensic or sports science investigation.

You will need to produce evidence to show that you have skillfully used laboratory techniques to carry out your investigation.

Whilst carrying out your investigation for **Unit 3** you will be expected to:
- Describe its purpose
- Produce a plan
- Complete a risk assessment
- Collect some results
- Carry out calculations
- Make conclusions
- Evaluate your work and explain how either a food, forensic or sports scientist might use the results of your investigation.

Your teacher will assess Unit 3 of the course as part of your coursework. Whilst completing your investigation you will need to use the Unit 3 assessment grid in the AQA Additional Applied Science specification. The assessment grid is divided into three stages; the checklist below details what should be included at each stage.

At Stage 1 you should state the purpose of the investigation, produce an appropriate plan, risk assessment and be able to select equipment. You should be able to collect some results from your investigation and give some conclusions and an evaluation.

To obtain higher marks at Stage 2 you should be able to demonstrate some independence in your work and describe its purpose. You should be able to interpret the results collected from your investigation and be able to comment on the reliability of your results. You should also be able to suggest an improvement to your investigation and explain how the improvement would help in collecting results that are more reliable. It is also important that you describe how either a food, forensic or sports scientist might use the results of your investigation.

To obtain the highest marks at Stage 3 you should carefully explain the purpose of your investigation. Your evidence should give a clear indication that you have carefully and independently planned your investigation and anticipated any problems that may occur. You should be able to work independently when selecting appropriate equipment and producing risk assessments. You should also be able to recognise when it is important to repeat an experiment, complete calculations, use and rearrange a mathematical equation. As well as giving conclusions and evaluations of your work it is important that you carefully explain how either a food, forensic or sports scientist might use the results of your investigation.

Chapter 3
Food science

Your health is dependent to some extent on your lifestyle, including the type of food you eat. In this chapter you will learn about some of the science and techniques used by food scientists and dieticians to help you maintain a healthy body and a healthy lifestyle. For example, a dietician studies an individual's diet, records their food consumption and nutritionally analyses their food intake. The dietician can then make recommendations for a healthier diet. In this chapter you will learn about:

- What a healthy diet should contain
- How to recognise healthy and unhealthy foods
- The importance of hygiene in food production
- How food is safely produced
- The environmental impact of food production

This chapter contains the theory you should learn to complete the food science questions for the Unit 2 examination. For your Unit 3 portfolio, you may complete one investigation using the theory from this chapter. Some investigations and portfolio works are included throughout this chapter that could contribute to your portfolio.

Chapter 3 is divided into six topics:

1 Food nutrients and their functions
2 Food additives
3 Food labelling and food testing
4 Useful microorganisms in the production of food
5 Microorganisms and food safety
6 Organic and intensive farming

1 Food nutrients and their functions

Our bodies are remarkable. If they were a car they would be classed as superior to a Mercedes Benz, a Bentley, a Porsche and an Isuzu all rolled into one.

Humans have the capacity to adapt to many extreme environments, and there are a huge variety of ways in which we use our bodies. There are gymnasts who can swing around poles athletically and there are swimmers who can dive to extreme depths. Either way, human bodies are all practically the same, and have the same potential. You can train and adapt your own body to do any number of amazing activities if you provide it with the correct fuel.

Figure 3.1 How are you feeling?

> **Nutrient**
> Something the body needs for energy, growth and to protect against disease; sometimes water is classed as a nutrient as it is essential for life
>
> **Respiration**
> The process that releases the energy in food – this energy is used by the body for movement, growth and chemical reactions inside cells

Fuel is needed for all activities; even sitting at your desk reading this uses energy and **nutrients**, which you need to replace to ensure that your body lasts. Just like car bodywork, your body needs constant maintenance, filling and polishing.

In this topic you will learn about:
- food nutrients and their functions;
- what happens if you don't get enough essential nutrients;
- what a healthy diet means.

1.1 Nutrients in food

For the Unit 2 written examination you need to know:
- that the human body requires a variety of nutrients in order to carry out the vital functions of life – **respiration**, movement, growth and repair of body tissue;

Figure 3.2 The good, the bad and the ugly – which foods are good sources of carbohydrates?

Figure 3.3 Footballers eat starchy carbohydrates for energy before a game.

❶ What other foods would be good carbohydrate providers for breakfast?

❷ Is there a difference between:
• Ricicles® and Rice Krispies?
• Cornflakes and Frosties?

Glycaemic index
A ranking system for carbohydrates based on their effect on blood sugar

• the function of the following nutrients
  – carbohydrates, as energy providers
  – saturated and unsaturated fats, for insulation, for energy provision, to provide a viable source of the fat-soluble vitamins (A, D, E, K), and to protect vital organs (such as the kidneys)
  – proteins, for repair of body tissues, growth and energy;
• symptoms of any vitamin deficiencies in the human body;
• examples of foods that are good sources of these nutrients;
• the importance of fibre in the diet.

When provided with appropriate information, you should also be able to use data, theories and explanations to:
• comment on the nutritional value of food;
• consider the impact of marketing, fast food and lifestyle on diet and health.

All human bodies need a source of nutrients to respire, move, grow and repair any damaged body tissue. The nutrients in food include carbohydrates, fats, proteins, vitamins and minerals.

Carbohydrates

Carbohydrates are thought of as 'fuel', or as providing energy.

Some fuels are better for you than others. For example, sugar in your tea, or sugar in sweets, cakes or desserts is quickly released into the bloodstream and provides you with a quick fix of energy. But in car language, you do not get many 'miles to the gallon' on simple carbohydrates like sugar. So sugar is often referred to as one of the 'bad' carbohydrates – all the energy is released quickly.

Sugar has other disadvantages. It causes tooth decay, and too much sugar can be responsible for the onset of diabetes.

The 'good' carbohydrates include starchy foods such as wheat, potatoes, pasta or brown rice. These all get much better 'miles to the gallon' as they release energy slowly over a longer period. They also do not cause tooth decay or diabetes. So for your body to work like a highly efficient sports car, it is important to eat the 'good' carbohydrates and not be tempted by the 'bad' carbohydrates. (High-carbohydrate diets in sports nutrition are described on page 170.)

You may have heard of the GI diet (GI stands for **glycaemic index**). It relies on a slow release of carbohydrates to fuel the body consistently and continually without any highs or lows in blood sugar. A 'diet' is just what you usually eat – the GI diet is not just about weight loss. A lot of celebrities use this eating programme to recover from illness. So next time you get porridge for breakfast, don't complain!

Essential fatty acid

A fatty acid that the body needs in order to work properly – the body cannot make it, so you have to eat it; found in oily fish

Saturated fat

Can raise blood cholesterol levels

Unsaturated fat

Can lower blood cholesterol levels

Polyunsaturated fat

A type of unsaturated fat that helps lower blood cholesterol and contains essential fatty acids

Fats

You will be relieved to know that it is a myth that fats are bad for you. In fact, it is essential you have some fat in your diet. Compounds called **essential fatty acids** have essential roles in the body and if you exclude fats from your diet you could affect your health.

However, as with carbohydrates, you are advised to choose your source of fats carefully. **Saturated fats** can raise blood cholesterol levels; **unsaturated fats** can lower blood cholesterol levels, and **polyunsaturated fats** also contain the essential fatty acids (see page 46). For example, put that chocolate éclair back down! Dairy products and red meats contain saturated fats. Instead, eat a variety of nuts such as peanuts, walnuts, brazil nuts and almonds, which have unsaturated fats and also contain a variety of other useful nutrients. Oily fish such as salmon and tuna, and olive oil, are also good sources of unsaturated fat.

The functions of fats

There are seven main functions of fats. Although fats have a role in the body, excess fat is still stored in the fatty tissues.

Figure 3.4 Foods high in saturated fat

Figure 3.5 Foods containing unsaturated fats

Figure 3.6 Are they cold?

Hypothermia

When your internal body temperature falls to below 35.5 °C you may suffer a gradual reduction in coordination of muscles and movement, and a falling level of consciousness

❸ Why do Eskimos require extra insulation?

❹ Why do you think seals have layers of blubber under their skin?

Satiety

A feeling of fullness. Does lettuce fill you up, or does a cream cake?

Figure 3.7 How long can they go on for?

If you were ever stranded on a desert island, would you rather be slightly plump or slightly skinny?

1 Providing insulation: fat layers help keep you warm in winter. This is very important – if your internal body temperature drops below 35.5 °C you are in danger of suffering from **hypothermia**. Extra insulation is especially useful if you don't have gas central heating in your house.

2 Providing a concentrated form of energy: fats are a source of energy, like carbohydrates, but there is more energy in fats than in the same amount of carbohydrate. You can also easily store fat to use later – carbohydrates provide an immediate energy source. You have to exercise for 20 minutes before you start to use up any of the stored fat.

3 Protecting vital organs: the layers of fat around your heart, liver and kidneys help to protect these organs from being damaged in falls, fights, etc.

4 Providing a source of fat-soluble vitamins (A, D, E, K): animal fats can leak out of the meat juices during the cooking process. Think of a chicken roasting in an oven. Why do you think the chef uses the juices to make the gravy? It is not just due to the flavour, but also because the gravy then has an increased nutrient content.

5 Providing a feeling of **satiety** or satisfaction: foods such as fruit and vegetables contain not only a high percentage of vitamin C, but also a high percentage of water. The water passes through the body quite quickly, which means you feel hungry again soon. Foods containing fat take a lot longer to pass through the digestive system and so stop you from getting hungry as quickly. This can help prevent snacking between meals. The Atkins diet uses this, and relies on the fact that you cannot physically consume too much fat as you will feel very full indeed.

6 Giving flavour to food: unfortunately for dieters, it is not a coincidence that food that tastes delicious has more fat in it. Fat adds flavour – especially in meat. Some people really enjoy the fat on the side of meat, such as the crispy crackling on pork.

7 Giving texture to food: the presence of fat can give foods a smooth, rich texture. This is why chefs such as Jamie Oliver recommend you put 20 g of butter in sauces such as gravy, cheese sauce or chocolate sauce. But this adds to the total energy content of the food. Rosemary Conley may have a coronary at the mere thought of that!

❺ Why do motorbike riders wear special back protectors?

Protein

Protein is a very important nutrient in all our diets, whatever our gender, age and level of activity. Protein is responsible for maintaining the efficient running, maintenance and repair of our bodies.

Protein can be used as a source of energy if there are not enough carbohydrates and fats in your diet – if you are starving. But first the body will use fats and carbohydrates for energy.

Figure 3.8 These foods are high in protein.

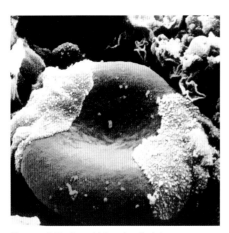

Figure 3.9 A red blood cell dying

> **RDA (Recommended Daily Allowance)**
> The minimum daily amount of a specific nutrient necessary for health

Weightlifters often believe they need a lot of protein to repair and strengthen their muscle. (High-protein diets in sports nutrition are described on page 170.) Although their protein requirement is slightly increased, your body can only absorb a limited amount of protein. So drinking too many concentrated protein shakes has little benefit as you drink them in and excrete the protein out.

Protein is used mainly to grow new cells, or to repair any body cells that are damaged or have died. Body cells may need replacing for many reasons – from falling over and grazing a knee in the park, to cutting yourself at work, to replacing dead cells. The average life of a red blood cell is only 120 days.

Vitamins and minerals

Your body needs many vitamins and minerals. These are required in varying amounts, which vary from person to person. However, there are guidelines to follow – called the **Recommended Daily Allowances** (RDAs).

Vitamins A, B, C, D, E and K are all different, and if you were to become a dietician – someone who advises people what to eat – you would study nutrition in a lot more detail at university. To give you an introduction to nutrition, Tables 3.1 and 3.2 outline the basic functions of some of the vitamins and minerals your body needs.

Figure 3.10 Eat me! Citrus fruits are a good source of vitamin C

Vitamin	What it does	Best sources
A	Assists in the normal growth of children – especially bones and teeth Keeps the skin healthy (useful to know for teenagers avoiding acne), and helps keep **mucous membranes** free from infection Assists in keeping eyes healthy and assisting vision in dim light: 'All the better to see you with,' said the big bad wolf	Liver and kidney, oily fish, green, orange and yellow vegetables, butter, egg yolk
B	Assists in the release of energy from carbohydrates to fuel the body Helps the human nerves function normally Vitamin B_{12} is needed to make red blood cells	Fortified breakfast cereals, bread and wholegrains, meat
C	Helps the body to absorb iron in food Helps skin to heal if it is damaged Helps the immune system to fight infection Essential for healthy skin, the tissue that makes blood vessels and cells in the lining of the digestive system	Vegetables, citrus fruits, blackcurrants
D	Promotes calcium and phosphorus absorption to help maintain strong teeth and bones	Liver, oily fish, milk, eggs
K	Helps your blood clot Helps platelets form when blood meets the oxygen in air – if your pet eats a batch of rat poison that contains warfarin, the vet will give an injection of vitamin K – rat poison works by thinning the blood, making the rats bleed internally, and a large dose of vitamin K counteracts this thinning of the blood	Green leafy vegetables

Table 3.1 The basic functions of the major vitamins

❻ Which vitamin helps the absorption of calcium?

❼ Why do you think hospitals now offer all newborn babies a vitamin K injection at birth?

Mucous membranes
The linings of the eyes, ears, nose, throat and lungs, which are kept moist – the mucus acts as a protective blanket to prevent pathogens from entering the body

Mineral	What it does	Best sources
Iron	Helps your body to make **haemoglobin** for red blood cells, which are needed to transport oxygen around the body so that tissues can respire and get the energy they need	Red meat, wholegrain and fortified cereals, green leafy vegetables such as spinach, pulses such as lentils and kidney beans, and some dried fruits
Calcium	Responsible for developing and maintaining healthy and strong teeth and bones – you can tell if someone is calcium-deficient by seeing if their fingernails are cracked, brittle and dry	Dairy foods (milk, yoghurt, cheese), leafy green vegetables
Phosphorus	Assists in ensuring you have strong teeth and bones Helps release energy from food	Meat, milk, wholegrains
Zinc	Helps enzymes in the body work and helps wounds to heal – extra zinc is also said to help with the white bits on your fingernails	Meat, dairy products, wholegrains, beans and lentils, peanuts

Table 3.2 The basic functions of the major minerals

> **Haemoglobin**
> The part of the red blood cells that carries oxygen

> **8** Are girls or boys more likely to suffer from anaemia during puberty? Why?
>
> **9** What combination of vitamins and minerals do you need in order to have healthy teeth, nails and bones?
>
> **10** What substance in your blood is responsible for transporting oxygen around the body?

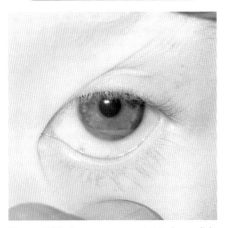

Figure 3.11 Are you anaemic? Pale eyelids could mean low levels of haemoglobin in the blood.

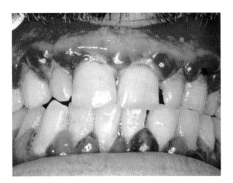

Figure 3.12 Would you want to look like this?

Vitamin deficiency

At first, if you do not consume enough vitamins your body will see if any are stored somewhere. It's a bit like having a bank account – you can store certain vitamins to use later. Not all, though: vitamins B and C are water-soluble and are very difficult to store because the excess is excreted in urine. But vitamins A and D are fat-soluble and can be stored in your fatty tissues and liver.

A vitamin deficiency may cause some changes in your body, or a deficiency disease. The onset of any symptoms will depend on storage levels and the amount of activity. Generally, a lack of the following vitamins will cause the following changes.

- Vitamin A – 'night blindness' or an inability to adjust to dim light; severe deficiency leads to dry eyes, cornea problems and even blindness.
- Vitamin B – you will start to feel really tired (onset of anaemia) and you may develop mouth sores. Deficiency for a prolonged period may also lead to nerve cell degeneration.
- Vitamin C – bleeding gums and loose teeth (sailors used to have a condition called scurvy that made their gums and teeth look particularly unattractive); cuts don't heal properly; decreased immunity (more colds); blood vessels become fragile and burst easily, causing bruising. Vitamin C is also responsible for helping the body absorb iron, so a lack of vitamin C can also be responsible for the onset of anaemia.
- Vitamin D – poor calcium absorption causes weak bones and teeth, leading to more risk of fractures. Vitamin D deficiency in children causes rickets or bone deformation, where weak bones cannot support the child's growing weight.

Table 3.3 gives some sources of common vitamins.

Nutrient	Portion size	Amount of nutrient per portion	Percentage of RDA
Vitamin A	One small snack bag of apricots (35 g)	85 µg	11%
Vitamin B₁	Portion of bran cereal (25 g)	0.25 mg	18%
Vitamin C	One orange (50 g)	25 mg	42%

Table 3.3 Some sources of common vitamins

> **11** How can you help preserve the vitamins that are fat-soluble or water-soluble during cooking?
>
> **12** Why do you think sailors in particular suffered from scurvy?
>
> **13** The elderly often suffer from lack of vitamin D and/or calcium.
> a) Why do you think this is?   c) What can it lead to?
> b) Why is this a problem?   d) What is the solution?

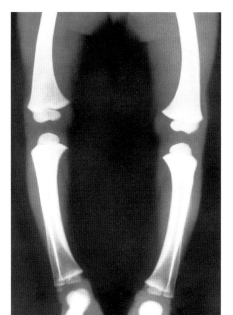

Figure 3.13 A child whose diet lacks vitamin D or calcium

> **Constipation**
> Inability to have a bowel movement as there is not sufficient lubrication for the muscles to move the waste along the intestinal tract
>
> **Balanced diet**
> A combination of food choices that gives the body all the nutrients needed for good health

Figure 3.14 Eat me too!

> ⑭ What are the health benefits of eating a lot of fibre?

Fibre

Fibre is not officially classed as a nutrient, as it is not essential for life and is not digested and absorbed. However, life can be very uncomfortable without it. You only have to stop consuming fibre for a couple of days to know the exact function of fibre.

Fibre is vital to your diet as it helps prevent **constipation** by absorbing water. It also helps to absorb toxins (poisonous wastes) left behind from digesting foods. The fibre absorbs the toxins and then passes out of the human body. Recent studies have shown that adults who consume a lot of fibre may lower their cholesterol level and so lower the risk of heart disease. A diet rich in fibre can also reduce the risk of developing bowel cancer.

Fibre is present in wholegrains (wholewheat bread, brown rice) and in fruit and vegetables, especially the skins. If you eat a sensible, **balanced diet** you should automatically consume enough fibre to keep your digestive system working well. The elderly are advised to eat more fibre, as their digestive tract is older and more tired, so may need a helping hand.

1.2 A balanced diet

For the Unit 2 written examination you need to know:
- the health risks of eating too much saturated fat, sugar and salt;
- the importance of controlling overall energy intake (energy requirements of different individuals, dieting).

The trick with your diet is 'balance'. Too much of anything is bad for you, as is too little. It's all about proportions. So you can pick that chocolate éclair back up – so long as you haven't just consumed a lot of other 'bad' carbohydrate and fat. If you had chips for lunch, you shouldn't also have the chocolate éclair. But if you had cereal for breakfast (without sugar), and fruit for lunch, then you deserve a little snack or treat occasionally. Some foods are fantastic as they contain large amounts of a range of useful nutrients.

For example:
- nuts contain protein, B vitamins, good sources of fats;
- oily fish contains good oils, protein, vitamins A and D, calcium and phosphorus;
- steak is a great source of protein and iron;
- cheese is a good source of protein, calcium and vitamin D.

Health risks from an unbalanced diet

Consuming too much saturated fat, sugar or salt can be harmful to your body. Although some of this harm could be permanent, good eating habits can reverse some changes.

For example, too much saturated fat means cholesterol levels in the blood can rise. Fatty deposits can form on the artery walls, making them narrower. This means it takes a greater amount of pressure to push

Figure 3.15 A chocolate éclair can be part of a balanced diet – so long as you also eat other foods with vitamins and fibre, and avoid too much fat.

Blood pressure
The pressure in your arteries caused by the heart pumping

Diabetes
There are two types of diabetes – type 1 develops very early in life; type 2 usually develops only later in life, because you have eaten too much sugar over a long time

You may have seen TV adverts promoting yoghurt drinks that are full of 'goodness', which can assist in lowering blood pressure. Would you drink them? Why?

15 How could you cut salt out of your diet totally? Is this advisable?

16 Think of snacks you might eat during the day, then think of some healthy alternatives you could consume instead.

the blood around your body. This forces up your **blood pressure** and could lead to a burst blood vessel or a stroke. High blood pressure also makes your heart work harder, and the greater strain on your heart increases the risk of a heart attack.

Eating healthily now can reduce your risk of stroke and heart disease as an adult. Replacing saturated fats with polyunsaturated fats can reduce your blood pressure. Eating lots of fruit and vegetables and lowering fat can help you lose weight, which decreases the strain on your heart.

Individuals who consume too much or too little fat (saturated and unsaturated) are likely to be off work more often than those who consume a healthy, balanced diet.

Too much salt in the diet also increases your blood pressure, and again causes your heart to work harder. Lowering the salt level in your diet can reverse the risks associated with high blood pressure.

Too much sugar, however, cannot necessarily be reversed. Sugar is the number one factor responsible for tooth decay, which unfortunately is not reversible. Once your teeth have rotted, that's it – you are doomed to have false teeth. Eating too much sugar is also responsible for the onset of type 2 **diabetes**. Although diabetes can be controlled through diet, it cannot be cured. There would be no giant chocolate bars for you any more.

Controlling total energy intake

There are health risks associated with too much saturated fat or too much sugar, but also with too much total energy. Daily energy requirements depend on age. Teenagers need more energy from food than adults, as they are still growing. Energy requirements also depend on gender, body mass and activity levels (see page 166).

The energy value of food is measured in joules or kilojoules (1 kJ = 1000 J). If too much carbohydrate or fat (too many calories) is consumed, compared with the amount of energy used in exercise, it is stored as body fat. A reduced-calorie diet is needed – but 'dieters' should still take care to follow a balanced diet.

Studies have shown that obesity is on the increase. It is believed that soon one in three men and women in the UK will be clinically obese. Obesity causes complications in operations, and therefore costs the NHS a lot of money. Obesity is also linked to an increased risk of heart disease and diabetes.

Should people who deliberately do not live a healthy lifestyle pay more for their medical treatment? Or should we all pay the same, and it is up to us how we live our lives? The National Health Service is funded by contributions taken from our wages, so should you pay to keep a smoker healthy? What about anorexics or obese people, or individuals who take drugs and alcohol?

Case Study – Food diaries

These food diaries belong to a group of four friends who go to school together. They all live along the same road and walk 10 minutes to school together in the morning and home again at the end of the day, but they have different lifestyles. Peter plays football at the weekend. Katy is vegetarian, she belongs to a running club and goes running three times a week. Molly doesn't believe in exercise, she likes to sit and play on the computer. John is an avid swimmer, he is training as he hopes to participate in the next Olympics, especially as they are now going to be held in England. He gets up early every morning and swims before walking to school.

Meal	Peter	Katy	Molly	John
Breakfast (eaten before school)	Bacon sandwich and fruit juice	Cereal bar	None	Four Weetabix with milk and a little sugar
Elevenses at school break	Crisps	Banana	None	Toasted teacake
Lunch	Pizza and chips Flapjack	Cheese sandwich and crisps Apple	Chips and beans	Jacket potato with chilli con carne
Snack in the afternoon	Nothing	Orange	Chocolate bar	Banana
Dinner at home in the evening	Soup Chicken risotto Garlic bread	Melon Lasagne Garlic bread	Fish and chips	Roast pork, roast potatoes, carrots, broccoli and gravy
Dessert	Treacle sponge and custard	Fresh fruit salad	Trifle	Apple pie and cream
Supper (just before going to bed)	Toast and jam	Nothing	Chocolate gateaux	Cheese and biscuits
Drinks throughout the day	Cola Fanta Lucozade	Milk Orange juice	Lemonade Blackcurrant juice	Orange juice Tea

Table 3.4 Food diary record

⑰ What foods do you think Peter is particularly missing? What deficiency will this lead to if his diet continues in this manner? What foods should he include or swap? Suggest three meal or snack alternatives.

⑱ What foods does a vegetarian not eat? Is there more than one type of vegetarian?

⑲ Which foods in her diet provide Katy with protein? What other foods could Katy eat to increase her protein intake?

⑳ Name five bad things about Molly's diet.

㉑ John is a very active young man. Name three nutrients his body really needs. Analyse his diet and say if you think he is getting enough of those nutrients. Can you make any suggestions to improve John's diet for that particular day?

㉒ Apart from diet, what else could Molly do to improve her general health?

㉓ Who eats healthy snacks? What are they?

㉔ Is a flapjack healthy? Explain your answer.

㉕ Do drinks count towards your healthy lifestyle? Why?

㉖ Who drinks good, useful liquids? Who does not?

㉗ What is the best liquid to drink? How much should you drink?

Figure 3.16 Processed food, like instant meals, often contain many additives.

2 Food additives

Today we are very fussy about our food. Food additives are chemicals that are put into food to improve a feature of the food so that it can be 'just right'.

In this topic you will learn about:
- why food additives are used;
- how additives in food are regulated;
- the possible drawbacks of using food additives.

2.1 Types of food additive

For the Unit 2 written examination you need to know:
- the function of, and examples of, the following additives – antioxidants, flavourings and flavour enhancers, colourings, preservatives, sweeteners, thickeners;
- some advantages of using additives (improved taste, appearance and shelf life).

Food additives are chemicals added to a food to perform a function. Generally people prefer the idea of using 'natural' additives as opposed to artificial ones.

All additives are thoroughly assessed for safety before they are allowed to be used in food. If additives have been accepted as safe for use within the European Union, they are given an '**E-number**'. Using E-numbers is simple and convenient. For example, E219 is called sodium methyl p-hydroxybenzoate – long names are sometimes difficult to fit on small food labels.

E-number
Permitted food additives in the European Union – 'E' stands for explanation

Natural additives are chemicals found naturally within a food, and can be extracted to be used in another food. For example; beetroot juice (E162) is used to colour sweets, jelly and even oxtail soup. Guar gum (E412) is found in some types of peas, and is used as a thickener in sauces. Sugar and salt are natural additives, but do not have E-numbers as they are classed as food themselves.

Artificial additives are not naturally present in foods, and are made synthetically. An example is azodicarbonamide (E927), which is used as a flour improver to help hold bread dough together. There are over 400 additives permitted in the European Union.

Food additives have a variety of uses and are split into groups. They are normally grouped by their function, in other words, by what they do to food. The main groups of food additives are described below.

Antioxidant
A substance added to food to prevent an oxidation reaction

Antioxidants

Have you ever tasted butter or margarine that has been in the fridge too long? It tastes rancid (metallic and sour). An **antioxidant** decreases the chance of oils and fats in foods reacting with oxygen from the air that turns them rancid. This alters the food colour and flavour. Antioxidants also have the advantage that they can be used to extend the shelf life of foods. Vitamin C (ascorbic acid) is one of the most widely used antioxidants.

Colourings

Have you ever seen anyone add bicarbonate of soda to a saucepan of green vegetables when cooking? This is to help them look better, by keeping the rich, dark green colour within the cabbage and, in theory, to make it look more appealing. During the manufacture of some foods, such as canned marrowfat peas, the overall colour can decrease or even be lost. This makes some foods look less attractive. Colourings are added to restore the original colour and make the food look better.

Colour additives can also be used to make the existing food colour brighter, for example, to enhance the yellowness of custard. Colourings can be natural, such as curcumin (E100, a yellow extract of turmeric roots) or artificial, such as tartrazine (another yellow colouring). Artificial colourings can also be made to be identical to nature. Some colours are also vitamins (such as riboflavin and beta-carotene) – these are the only colourings allowed in baby foods.

> **28** What is the name of the type of reaction that fats undergo when they react with the air?

> **29** Why do you think only certain colours are allowed to be used in baby food?
>
> **30** Study some ingredient lists on food labels to see which colours are used. Classify them as natural, nature-identical or artificial. Which would you prefer manufacturers to use? Why?

Nirvana Custard

Ingredients:
Skimmed milk, buttermilk, sugar, modified starch, vegetable oil, whey, flavouring, colours (curcumin, amatto). Total milk content 73%.

✔ No artificial colours
✔ No preservatives
✔ A low fat food

Bez's BEANS

Ingredients:
Beans, tomatoes, water, sugar, glucose-fructose syrup, modified cornflour, salt, spirit vinegar, spice extracts, herb extracts, artificial colouring.

Bouncing Baby Food

Ingredients:
Yoghurt, fresh orange juice, pureed strawberries, mashed bananas.

Figure 3.17 Examples of some food labels

Practical Work – Assessing the mix of colours in sweets

Equipment
- Sweets/food colourings
- Cocktail sticks
- Filter paper/chromatography paper
- Pencil
- Ruler
- Beaker
- Watch glass
- Distilled water
- Chromatography clips/paper clips
- Cling film
- Lemon juice (for extension work)

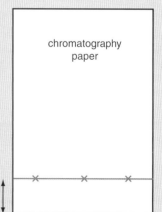

Procedure

1 Draw a pencil line 1 cm up from the bottom across a piece of chromatography paper (see diagram) and place two or three (depending on how many different sweets or colours you are studying) small crosses along the line – evenly spaced out, and not too close to the edge.

2 Place the sweet on the watch glass, and add a small amount of distilled water to dissolve the colour (food colours are obviously already a liquid so do not need any water adding).

3 Dip the cocktail stick into the colour on the watch glass and place the tip onto one of the small crosses. Allow the drop to dry, add two or three more drops exactly on top of one another and allow the drops to fully dry.

4 Repeat for the other colours on other small crosses.

5 Put some distilled water into a beaker until the depth is approximately 2 cm. Suspend the filter paper so that just the bottom of the filter paper is dipping into the water. Hold firmly in place (see diagram). Remember to ensure the filter paper is not touching the sides of the beaker.

6 Put cling film over the top of the beaker.

Extension

Take a piece of filter paper. Write a secret message using a cocktail stick dipped in lemon juice. Give it to a friend – they can discover the message by warming it over a radiator.

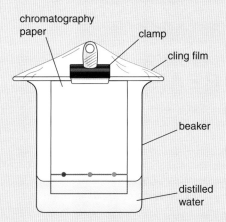

Analyse the results

- Look how far each of the colours has travelled up the filter paper. Compare these. Do they move the same distance?
- What other things could you use this procedure for?

31 Why must the filter paper not touch the side of the beaker?

32 Why must you allow the drops to dry before adding any more?

33 What happens if the filter paper is suspended in the beaker so that the pencil line is below the surface of the water?

> **Preservatives**
> Chemicals added to food so that it does not spoil

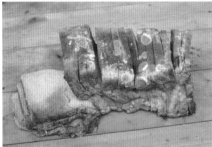

Figure 3.18 Which would you choose to eat?

---

34 Why do you think people like food products to have a long shelf life?

35 Do the supermarket own-brand squashes have artificial sweeteners or sugar in them? Why do you think this is?

36 When might you use thickeners in your own kitchen?

Preservatives

Foods 'spoil' when bacteria multiply and produce toxins (see page 68), so food preserving works by killing microorganisms (for example by heat or acid) or by slowing down their rate of growth. Freezing, canning or drying can all preserve foods and so increase the time food can be stored safely – the shelf life. Chemical **preservatives** are also used to help improve the overall shelf life of a food product. Benzoic acid is a common food preservative.

Any processed food with a long shelf life is likely to include added preservatives, unless it is dried, tinned or frozen. Traditional methods using sugar, salt and vinegar are still used to preserve some foods. The use of preservatives helps to decrease the overall cost of food production, as it reduces wastage. Foods can also be transported more easily.

Other food additives

Flavour enhancers are used widely in savoury foods to make the existing flavour in the food stronger. Monosodium glutamate is an example of a flavour enhancer. This is often used in Chinese takeaway food.

Sweeteners are used instead of sugar. Do you consume regular or diet drinks? Diet drinks contain artificial sweeteners such as aspartame. Saccharin and aspartame are many times sweeter than sugar – a tiny amount produces the same sweet taste. This makes them suitable for use in products such as diet drinks, which are very low in energy. It also makes them economical to use, as they are only needed in small quantities. However, recently there have been several health scares about artificial sweeteners.

Emulsifiers, stabilisers, gelling agents and thickeners improve the texture or consistency of a food. Emulsifiers help mix together ingredients such as oil and water, that would normally separate. For example, in mayonnaise, stabilisers prevent oil and vinegar from separating again. Gelling agents are used to give foods a gel-like consistency, while thickeners increase the viscosity of foods. The most common thickener is starch.

How are food additives controlled?

Additives are thoroughly assessed for possible toxic effects before they are permitted for food use. Each additive is also permitted in only a limited number of foods. The European Food Safety Authority looks at the results of a large number of tests on humans and animals before permitting a new additive.

Additives accepted as safe for use within the European Union are given an E-number. A number with no 'E' means the additive has been approved by the UK, but not yet by the European Union. Even when an additive has been approved, food scientists continually check the safe levels. If scientists learn more about the effect of certain chemicals in our bodies, or people's eating habits change so they eat more of a certain food each day, the safety advice might change.

The Food Standards Agency and local authorities routinely test food products for banned chemicals, or check that additives are not above the legal limit.

Additives are always in the media spotlight. For example, in 2005 there was a health scare about Sudan I, a dye used to colour shoe polish red. It is not permitted as a food colouring, as experiments have shown that it could cause cancer in laboratory animals. Importers must have a certificate showing that their food is free of Sudan I. In 2005 the dye was found in food by Italian food inspectors. The illegally dyed chilli powder was used in a wide range of food products, and there had to be a **product recall** of over 400 products sold in UK supermarkets.

Product recall
A request that an entire batch is removed from shops and returned to the manufacturer because of safety concerns

The Food Standards Agency has information on additives currently allowed in foods, and their E-numbers, at www.food.gov.uk; the latest news on product recalls and food alerts is at www.food.gov.uk/enforcement

37 Are all additives listed on food labels? Why?

38 Why do you think government agencies test the new additives, not the companies that produce the additives?

39 If there is a problem with an additive, how quickly do you think the general public should be informed?
a) What would happen if there was a delay?
b) What would happen if the warning was quick, but didn't give many details about the risk?
c) Make a list of different ways the safety warning could be issued.

40 Do you think that the use of additives is controlled sufficiently? Give reasons for your answer.

2.2 Are all E-numbers bad?

For the Unit 2 written examination you need to know:
- some disadvantages of using additives (toxic nature of some preservatives; hyperactivity linked to tartrazine).

41 Do you want additives used in your food? Give reasons for your answer.

42 Which of the functions of food additives in Table 3.5 do you think are the most important? Why?

When provided with appropriate information you should also be able to use data, theories and explanations to:
- consider the social and economic impact of information about the long-term harmful effects of eating certain types of food, or food containing certain types of additive.

E-number	Additive	Function	Examples of foods
E100	Curcumin	Colourings (yellow)	Coloured fizzy drinks
E102	Tartrazine		Fruit squash
			Yellow cakes
E210	Benzoic acid	Preservatives – prevent the growth of bacteria	Fruit juice
E249	Nitrite		Cured meats, e.g. ham, bacon
E220	Sulfur dioxide		
			Dried fruits, e.g. apricots
E300	Ascorbic acid	Antioxidants	Fatty foods to stop them from going rancid, e.g. salad dressings, meat pies
E320	Butylated hydroxyanisole		
E950	Acesulfame-K	Sweeteners	Soft drinks
E951	Aspartamine		Low-calorie desserts
E420	Sorbitol		
E621	Monosodium glutamate	Flavour enhancer	Chinese takeaways

Table 3.5 Examples of food additives and their functions

Advantages of using additives

Additives are used for a range of functions, including:
- keeping food safe until it is eaten, or improving the shelf life;
- improving the appearance of a food product;
- improving the taste of a food;
- fortifying a food to make it healthier;
- aiding food processing and manufacture by helping ingredients to bind.

In addition, using additives can reduce the overall cost of food production.

Disadvantages of using additives

Although additives do have a role in the food manufacturing industry, they can cause a reaction in some people, such as a skin rash, migraine or an asthma attack.

Some studies have linked artificial colourings, including tartrazine (E102), to increased hyperactivity in young children. Some of these food colourings are banned in other countries. But scientific experts agree that it is difficult to draw firm conclusions from the tests that have been carried out so far.

Some people think that eating foods containing preservatives over a long time may be harmful to human health. Benzoic acid preservatives could make asthma symptoms worse in people who already have asthma. Nitrite and sulfite preservatives may react with other compounds in foods to produce toxic substances.

Case Study – Schools rule out food additives

Seventy different additives including artificial colourings, sweeteners and preservatives were removed from primary school lunches prepared by a school catering firm in 2005. Hampshire County Council Catering Services (HC3S) supplies school lunches for 550 primary schools each day. They made the decision to remove the additives after working with the charity Hyperactive Children's Support Group's (HACSG). The charity promotes a dietary approach to dealing with children's hyperactivity. The firm was the first organisation to be awarded HACSG's highest award for excellence. Other school catering firms have also contacted HACSG for help in removing food additives from school meals.

Councillor Ken Thornber, leader of Hampshire County Council, said: 'There is no doubt in my mind that what children eat not only affects their physical health but also has an impact on their behaviour and concentration. The removal of additives from the menu is an important step and is part of a larger improvement plan for school meals.' Nick Giovinelli, from HACSG, added: 'We hope that other school catering organisations will be keen to follow Hampshire's fine example.'

www.hants.gov.uk/caterers/additives.html

43 How many different additives are to be removed from children's meals?
44 Name the registered charity that has been campaigning for the removal of additives.
45 Who else wanted the removal of additives?
46 Who is going to remove the additives?
47 What effects do some people believe the additives have? Why do you think this is a problem?

You decide

There is often a lot of media attention about additives. Bad news and frightening stories sell well. Who will buy a newspaper to read that what we are eating is 'safe'? The headline 'Risk of cancer from eating....' dramatically increases the sales of newspapers. Sometimes the evidence is not clear. If it can't be decided whether a certain food additive is safe or not, it is best for each person to make their own decision about whether to eat that food.

Food labels give information about all additives present so that consumers can make informed choices. As a consumer, you have the choice about which food to buy. Additives are usually found in processed food, so you can avoid consuming foods with lots of E-numbers if you always make your food from fresh ingredients.

Who is responsible for the increased use of additives? The food industry only responds to consumer demand. If people want their loaf of bread to last a full week, so that busy working families only have to shop once a week, then the food industry will develop the preservatives to stop loaves going mouldy (see Figure 3.18 on page 51).

Case Study – Food firm is fined over labelling

In 2006, a food importer was fined £5000 for incorrectly labelling a meatball product as gluten-free. This could potentially have affected the health of consumers who suffer from gluten intolerance.

Northamptonshire County Council's trading standards team carried out an investigation following a complaint from a customer. Mrs Harris bought the 'Swedish Chef – Authentic Swedish Meatballs' from a Tesco store in Northampton. She had checked the packaging and found that despite it being labelled 'this product does not contain lactose or gluten', the ingredients list included milk and breadcrumbs. As a result of the investigation, Tesco withdrew the product from all its stores and displayed posters informing customers of the problem with the meatball products. Rohi International Ltd imports meatballs from a Swedish manufacturer and sells them to supermarkets. The company pleaded guilty to two offences under the General Food Regulations 2004 at Northampton Magistrates Court. The firm was fined £2500 for each offence and ordered to pay £1289 costs.

Northampton Councillor Liz Tavener said 'Thanks to a successful investigation by the county council's trading standards service, these products were removed from the shelves and steps have now been taken by Rohi to ensure that food they are importing meets relevant safety requirements.'

48 What was the total financial cost to the company of mislabelling the Swedish meatballs?
49 What other costs might be incurred by the company?
50 Why was the mislabelling a problem?
51 Which ingredients contained the gluten?
52 Which ingredient contained the lactose?
53 Design a poster that Tesco could have used.
54 If you were the manager of Tesco, what would you have done when you had discovered the problem?

3 Food labelling and food testing

Food analysts test food to check that the information given on the label is correct.

In this topic you will learn about:
- how to interpret food labels;
- how to test and analyse some foods.

3.1 Food labels

For the Unit 2 written examination you need to be able to:
- interpret food labels, including sell-by dates, quantities, and energy values of nutrients and other components of food, including food additives.

The Food Labelling Regulations Act of 1996 covers pre-packaged foods to be sold as part of a business. (The Act does not cover food for the armed forces, for example.)

All food labels must show:
- name of the food;
- list of ingredients in order of greatest weight first;
- shelf life of the product;
- storage instructions;
- name and address of the manufacturer, packer or retailer responsible.

For some people, the information on the label is essential to help them avoid certain ingredients on health, religious or ethical grounds. Nutrition information also helps people make choices to help improve their health.

Nutrition information

Nutritional labelling is not compulsory. But if a manufacturer makes a nutritional claim on the package or in advertising (e.g. low fat, low sodium), they have to give certain information in a standard form, 'per 100 g' (see for example Figure 3.19 on page 57). Nutrition claims can only be made about energy values, protein, carbohydrate, fat, fibre, sodium and vitamins.

Claims about vitamins and minerals must show the percentage of the RDA (see page 42). It is not compulsory to show the recommended daily maximum amounts of salt and fat, but it is compulsory to show the amounts of these nutrients in the product.

Energy values quoted on the nutritional information panel show the energy content of a food in joules or kilojoules (kJ). In some cases the old units, kilocalories (kcal), are still used. 1 kcal is 4.2 kJ.

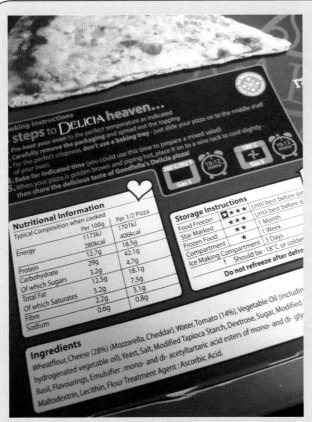

55 What beneficial nutrients are in this product?

56 List all the food additives in this product, then group them into types of additives.

57 How much of this food would you have to eat to exceed the RDA of 76 g for fat?

58 What other two pieces of information might, in certain cases, be on the label of a food product?

Figure 3.19 Ingredients and nutrition label for pizza

Other regulations state that all foods or food ingredients containing genetically modified soya or maize should be clearly labelled.

Shelf life

The food labelling laws say that all packaged food sold must have a date label. There are two types:
- best before – the period for which a food should keep its optimum condition and not go stale, for example biscuits, crisps;
- use by – for perishable foods that usually need to be kept cold, such as meat, fish, dairy products, ready-to-eat salads.

Case Study – Inaccurate labels on children's food

Tests on food aimed at children revealed that one in four products tested had incorrect nutritional information on packaging. Trading Standards officers across the East Midlands found and analysed 203 products aimed at children, often with cartoon characters on the labels. Of the samples tested, 53 were unsatisfactory. The main problem was errors in the nutritional information. Some had much more sugar or salt than was listed on the packaging.

One packet of crisps contained 150% more sugar than stated. One product contained 50% more saturated fat than declared, despite being labelled 'low in saturated fat'. Undeclared or non-permitted additives were also found in some samples.

Peter Heafield, County Trading Standards Officer for Lincolnshire said 'We will continue to monitor the situation and cannot rule out taking legal action against those businesses who are misleading parents about the quality of their children's foods'.

59 Which group of consumers did the products mainly affect?
60 If the packet of crisps said it had 12 g of sugar in it, how much did it really have?
61 Is it a problem when the wrong nutrient or additive is declared? Explain your answer.
62 Why might an additive be undeclared?
63 Why might an additive be illegal?
64 What was the percentage of unsatisfactory results?

3.2 Food testing

For the Unit 2 written examination you need to be able to describe and interpret:

- qualitative food tests for starch, fat, protein and reducing sugar and acidity;
- quantitative tests on food and food supplements –
  - moisture content by evaporation
  - suspended matter by filtration
  - acidity of a product by titration
  - vitamin C content of food
  - iron content of food supplements.

When provided with appropriate information you should to be able to:

- evaluate data from qualitative and quantitative analyses of food.

Qualitative analysis
Procedure to determine the identity of a substance using a series of simple chemical tests

Simple chemical tests can be used to help identify substances present in food. This is **qualitative analysis**. Qualitative tests identify the different substances present in a sample.

Practical Work – Qualitative food tests

Testing for reducing sugar (glucose)

Safety
- Wear eye protection.
- The very hot water bath can be boiling water from a kettle.

1 Set up apparatus as shown in the diagram.
2 Use $3\,cm^3$ of the test substance.
3 Add $3\,cm^3$ Benedict's solution to the test tube in the water bath. Leave for a few minutes.
4 Note any reaction changes.

If there is any reducing sugar present, the solution will turn orange/yellow when heated through.

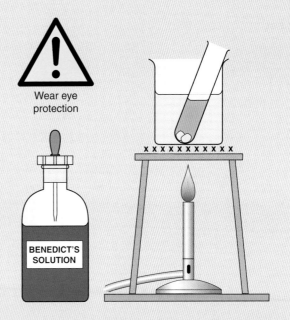

Wear eye protection

BENEDICT'S SOLUTION

Testing for starch

Safety
- Wear eye protection.
- Heating can be achieved by placing the test tube in boiling water from the kettle.

1 Crush the food.
2 Add a small amount to a boiling tube.
3 Add $5\,cm^3$ distilled water, and stir.
4 Heat gently for 1 minute.
5 Add a few drops of iodine solution to the food.

If there is any starch present, the solution will turn blue–black.

Testing for fat

Safety
- No naked flames should be present during this procedure.
- Wear eye protection.

1 Set up apparatus as shown in the diagram.
2 Use $3\,cm^3$ of the test substance.
3 Add five drops of ethanol to the test tube containing the suspected fat. Place a bung in it, and shake.
4 Add five drops of water, replace the bung and shake again.

If fat is present, a white cloudy emulsion will form.

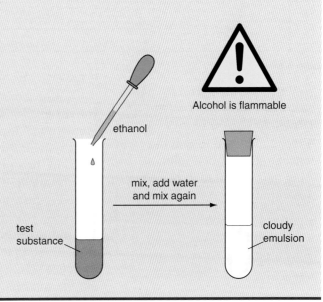

Alcohol is flammable

ethanol

test substance

mix, add water and mix again

cloudy emulsion

Practical Work – continued

Testing for protein

Safety
- Wear eye protection.
- Goggles should be worn if the concentration of sodium hydroxide is greater than 0.5 M.

1 Set up the apparatus as shown in the diagram.
2 Use 3 cm³ of the test substance.
3 Add five drops of Biuret solution to the test tube.

The blue solution turns purple in the presence of protein.

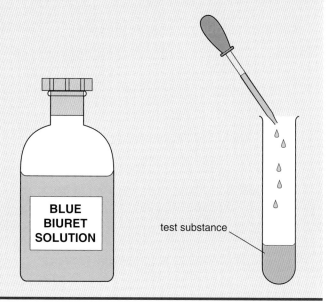

BLUE
BIURET
SOLUTION

test substance

Testing for acidity

pH
A scale for measuring acidity and alkalinity – acids have a pH below 7, and alkalis have a pH above 7

The acidity or alkalinity of liquids, and of sticky foods such as pickles, can be measured on the **pH** scale with universal indicator. This is a mixture of dyes that change colour when mixed with solutions of acid or alkali.

Each colour is matched to a pH number. The colours of universal indicator are given in Table 3.6.

Colour	Red	Orange	Yellow	Green	Dark green	Blue	Purple
pH	0–2	3–4	5–6	7	8–9	10–11	12–14
	← More acidic			Neutral	More alkaline →		

Table 3.6 The colours of universal indicator

Titration
A technique used to find the concentration of one solution, using another solution of known concentration

Standard solution
A solution of known concentration

The pH test for acidity relies on recognising a colour difference. If two people write down different pH numbers for the same colours, the test is not reliable. A more reliable method that can be repeated is to do a **titration**. In a titration experiment there are two solutions – one acid and one alkali. The concentration of one of the solutions is known, and is used to measure the concentration of the other solution.

A **standard solution** is made up with chemicals of the highest purity available so that the concentration is accurately known. It is the reference solution. The chemical is weighed as accurately as possible and the solution is prepared in a volumetric flask. A pipette is used to measure a fixed volume of the first solution into a conical flask. During the titration, a burette is used to measure how much of the second solution is needed to neutralise the first solution.

Other titrations

The quantitative tests for iron and vitamin content of foods are also titrations. The test substance is titrated against a solution that shows a colour change when all the ions in the test solution have been oxidised or reduced. For example, the calcium or iron content of foods can be determined by titration with a solution of potassium permanganate. The end point is when the solution changes from pale pink to purple. The calcium or iron content is determined from the volume of permanganate solution of known concentration that is required to reach the end point.

Practical Work – Finding the iron content of food supplements

In this investigation you will find out how much iron there is in a food supplement tablet, and compare this with the amount given on the bottle. If you extend this practical, you could use it as an investigation for Unit 3.

When measuring volumes of liquids, remember always to read to the bottom of the meniscus. Select a suitable size of container for the volume of liquid being measured – for example, don't use a $100\,cm^3$ measuring cylinder to measure only $5.5\,cm^3$ of liquid.

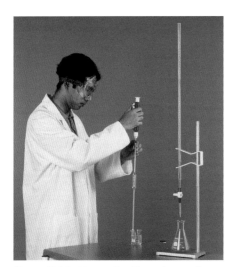

Figure 3.20 Measuring the volume of a standard solution accurately for a titration experiment

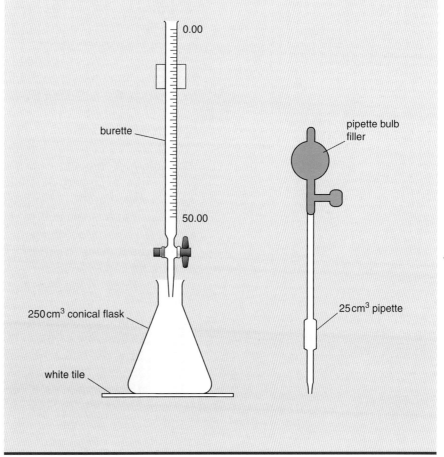

Equipment
- Iron tablets
- $250\,cm^3$ beaker
- Sulfuric acid (1 M)
- Pestle and mortar
- Balance
- $250\,cm^3$ volumetric flask
- $150\,cm^3$ conical flask
- Potassium manganate(VII) solution ($0.01\,M/dm^3$)
- Burette
- White tile
- Funnel
- Stand, boss and clamp
- $25\,cm^3$ pipette
- Pipette filler

Safety
- Wear eye protection.
- Consider wearing gloves when pouring potassium manganate(VII) into a burette. The stains are not harmful and will wear off in time.

Procedure
1 Crush five iron tablets in a pestle and mortar.
2 Weigh the empty beaker.
3 Transfer the crushed iron tablets to the beaker.
4 Reweigh the beaker to calculate the mass of the crushed tablets.
5 Dissolve the tablets in the beaker in a minimum amount of sulfuric acid (the coating may not dissolve).
6 Transfer this solution to a $250\,cm^3$ volumetric flask and add distilled water to the $250\,cm^3$ mark. This is your standard solution. You could work out its concentration in grams of solid per cubic decimetre of solution (g/dm^3).
7 Check the burette valve is closed. Fill your burette with the potassium manganate(VII) solution to the zero mark.
8 Use $25\,cm^3$ of the standard solution to titrate against the potassium manganate(VII) solution. The end point is when a faint pink–purple colour appears – there is then an excess of manganate(VII) ions present. (At the end point all the iron ions in the test solution have reacted with and decolorised the potassium manganate(VII) solution, so the excess manganate(VII) ions make the solution pink again.)
9 Read from the burette the amount of potassium manganate(VII) solution used. This is your titre.
10 Repeat the titration until your titres are within $0.2\,cm^3$.
11 Using the graph, calculate the amount of iron per tablet from the average titre and compare it with the amount stated on the label of the container.

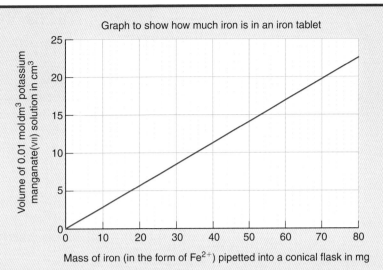

Graph to show how much iron is in an iron tablet

y-axis: Volume of 0.01 mol dm^3 potassium manganate(VII) solution in cm^3

x-axis: Mass of iron (in the form of Fe^{2+}) pipetted into a conical flask in mg

65 Use the graph above to calculate how much iron is in the tablet. Remember that you used five tablets, and sampled only 25 cm^3 of the standard solution at a time.

66 Evaluate the procedure. What could you do to improve the practical? What constraints were you working under and how did you solve the problems?

Ingredients labels have to show the amount of ingredients in weight order, including the weight of water in the finished product. A simple drying test can measure the mass before and after, assuming the only mass lost is the mass of the water.

Practical Work – Finding the water content of food

You can use this method to estimate the water content of a range of processed foods.

Procedure
1 Use a sample of about 100 g of food.
2 Grind the food in a pestle and mortar.
3 Weigh the sample as accurately as possible and record the mass in grams.
4 Spread the sample onto a large, flat dish and place in a drying oven set at 100 °C for 24 hours.
5 Weigh the dried samples again, and record the mass.
6 Repeat until the mass of dried food stays constant for two weighings.
7 Calculate the mass decrease as a percentage of the original mass of the food.

Food analysts also check that additives such as preservatives or colours are those permitted, and do not exceed specified levels. The chromatography test on pages 49–50 is used to identify what colourings are present.

The levels of all minerals in natural mineral water must be listed on the label. The amount of suspended matter, for example sand and mud, in bottled mineral water can be measured by filtration.

4 Useful microorganisms in the production of food

In this topic you will learn about:
- how some microorganisms are used in the production of food;
- what factors affect the growth of microorganisms, and how this growth can be controlled.

4.1 Fermentation

For the Unit 2 written examination you need to:
- describe the use of bacteria, yeast and other fungi in food production (bread, wine, beer, yoghurt and cheese).

Bacteria are very useful in the food industry, as well as being a nuisance. You will probably have sampled some of these useful products. For example, yoghurt, cheese and bread are produced using bacteria, and alcohol uses yeast (a fungus).

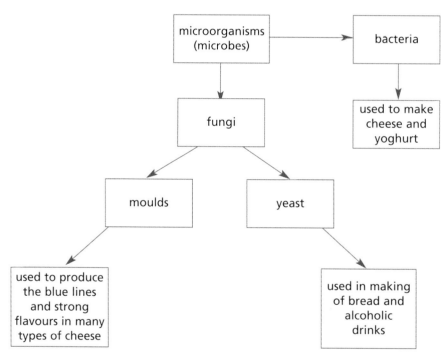

Figure 3.21 Foods and drinks made using microorganisms

When microorganisms respire anaerobically (without oxygen), they produce products that can be used to make food and drink. Fermentation is the type of anaerobic respiration used by yeast.

In the production of wine, beer and cider, fermentation by yeast changes sugar into alcohol. The carbon dioxide is removed unless the drink needs to be fizzy. In wine making, the source of sugar is the natural sugar in fruit such as grapes. In beer making, the source of sugar is barley. But even the specially selected yeasts can't break down the barley until it has been malted and mashed. This process breaks down the starch in barley into simple sugars such as glucose, which can be digested more easily by enzymes in the yeast.

The equation for fermentation of yeast is:

$$\text{Sugar} \rightarrow \text{alcohol (ethanol)} + \text{carbon dioxide} + \text{energy}$$
$$C_6H_{12}O_6 \rightarrow 2CH_3CH_2OH + 2CO_2 + 2ATP$$

There are other uses for fermentation, including the following.
- The carbon dioxide produced during fermentation is used in bread making. The gas bubbles trapped in the dough make it rise. The alcohol produced evaporates during baking in the oven.
- Another form of anaerobic respiration is used when lactic bacteria change the sugar in milk into lactic acid in the production of yoghurt. The bacteria break down the sugar in the milk to lactic acid, making the milk go thicker and slightly sour.
- Cheese is also made by fermenting milk with bacteria. An enzyme called rennet is added after the bacteria have produced lactic acid. Rennet makes the milk proteins turn solid.

67 What microorganism is used to produce beer?

68 What microorganism is used to produce yoghurt?

69 Produce a flow chart to show the production of yoghurt from milk.

70 What factors do you think it is important to control when fermenting alcohol?

Figure 3.22 Checking the temperature of a vat of milk used to make cheese

There are many practicals you can do to investigate factors that affect the rate at which fermentation occurs:

- yeast contains enzymes – if the temperature is too low, the enzymes do not work fast enough to produce a good yield;
- if the temperature is too high, the enzymes are destroyed;
- there must be a supply of sugar;
- air must be excluded, so the reaction can take place without oxygen (anaerobically).

Practical Work – Investigating the rate of fermentation in dough

Apparatus
- Flour
- Sugar
- Yeast mixture
- Measuring cylinder (50 cm^3)
- Stop watch
- Beaker
- Glass rod/spatula

Procedure
1 Weigh out 20 g of flour and 1g of sugar, and place in a 250 ml beaker.
2 Using a measuring cylinder, measure out 20 cm^3 of yeast mixture.
3 Pour the yeast mixture into the beaker and stir in thoroughly with a spatula or glass rod.
4 Pull the dough out of the beaker and knead the dough in your hands for 5 minutes. Place the dough into a 50 cm^3 measuring cylinder. Start the stop watch immediately and record the volume of the measuring cylinder every 3 minutes.

Repeat the above procedure, but vary **one** factor – the amount of sugar; or the amount of yeast; or the temperature of the water used to make the yeast solution.

Draw a graph of the results and compare. Plot the horizontal x-axis along the bottom and label it 'Time in minutes', as this is the factor you know. Label the vertical y-axis 'Volume in cm^3', as this is the factor you are measuring. Remember to put a title on your graph – 'A graph to show the volume of dough produced against time'.

What conclusions can you draw?

71 What makes the dough rise?
72 Did it start to rise immediately? If not, after how long? Why do you think this was?

73 Why do you think the sugar needs to be added?

74 What other factor could be important when trying to repeat the practical?

75 How could you prove that the activity of the yeast cells was responsible for making the dough rise?

4.2 Making use of moulds

The blue veins in cheeses such as stilton and gorgonzola are made by mould growing inside the cheese. The mould – a fungus called *Penicillium roqueforti* – grows along needle holes inserted into the cheese.

5 Microorganisms and food safety

Bacteria in food and drink can be harmful, and it is important to control or prevent the growth of bacteria that could get into food and cause food poisoning. Quality assurance managers in the food industry are responsible for hygiene control, as are cleaners and nurses in hospitals. Public health inspectors and environmental health officers working for local authorities inspect the food hygiene of businesses that prepare food for the public.

In this topic you will learn about:
- what causes food poisoning;
- how to prevent food poisoning by good hygiene;
- some ways to control the growth of bacteria;
- tests that show the level of bacteria in food.

For the Unit 2 written examination you need to know:
- examples of bacteria that cause food poisoning (*Salmonella*, *Escherichia coli*, *Campylobacter*);
- optimum conditions for the growth of bacteria (warmth, moisture, food source);
- common symptoms of food poisoning (stomach pains, vomiting, diarrhoea).

When provided with appropriate information, you should be able to:
- consider the problems of contamination of food products that have led to product recalls or health scares.

5.1 Food poisoning

There are at least a million cases of reported food poisoning in the UK each year. Many cases are not reported. If a doctor discovers a case of food poisoning, he/she is required to notify the local authority. The environmental health team looks at all cases reported and helps to identify if a food premises is implicated, as quickly as possible.

Food poisoning is caused by eating food contaminated by certain bacteria, or the toxins produced by the bacteria. The symptoms usually occur within the first 48 hours, and patients usually recover in a few days – but in a few severe cases, death can occur.

The symptoms are not nice at all – you usually remember a bad case of food poisoning. Symptoms include:
- feverish (feeling hot and cold) with or without a headache;
- either a feeling of sickness or actually being sick;
- diarrhoea with accompanying stomach pains or cramps.

However, similar symptoms could be produced by a hangover. That is why a case of food poisoning can't be confirmed without a sample of vomit or faeces being given to a doctor for testing by a microbiologist.

Most microorganisms are harmless – and some are used in industry to produce food and drinks. However, some bacteria can cause severe symptoms if they multiply in food. The main food poisoning bacteria are:
- *Salmonella* species;
- *Escherichia coli* (*E. coli*);
- *Clostridium* species;
- *Campylobacter* species.

The bacteria produce toxins (poisons) that are released into the food. It is the toxins, not the bacteria, that cause the symptoms and make you feel ill. This means it is possible for food that appears fresh and safe to contain the toxin. Even if the food has been treated to kill the microorganisms, for example by cooking or irradiation with gamma rays, it can still contain the toxin.
- Don't buy food that has gone past its sell-by date, as microorganisms may already be growing in the food.

Newspapers often publicise serious outbreaks of food poisoning that can be traced to a restaurant or fast-food takeaway. One fast-food worker could spread food poisoning bacteria to hundreds of customers.

76 Why do you think the reporting and investigating of food poisoning cases needs to happen quickly?

77 Why do people eat the food if it will make them ill?

78 The number of reported food poisoning cases is increasing. Why do you think this is, if education about hygiene practices has also improved?

Figure 3.23 The symptoms of food poisoning are thoroughly unpleasant.

79 As an activity, carry out research on an example of each of the food poisoning bacteria listed. You should find out the date of incidence and number of people affected. What bacteria caused the outbreak? What could have prevented it?

80 What is the problem for restaurants and food industries regarding outbreaks of bacteria? After all, people usually get better quite quickly.

Case Study – £1.2 million compensation for food poisoning

A Scottish woman won more than £1.2 million in compensation after food poisoning from eating a meal at a Chinese restaurant ruined her health. Margaret-Ann Reynard suffered severe arthritis triggered by salmonella food poisoning, leaving her unable to walk without a stick and unable to work as a midwife.

Mrs Reynard had gone to the Latours restaurant in East Kilbride in October 2000 with her fiancé to celebrate her 35th birthday. She felt fine afterwards but the next day felt ill and did not go to work. On the third evening she was admitted to hospital and suffered 17 days of diarrhoea. She ended up with inflamed and painful joints. Tests later showed the presence of the salmonella infection, and that the inflammation was triggered by the bacterial infection.

The judge who awarded damages said the former midwife was now in 'constant pain'. He awarded Mrs Reynard £1 243 082 in damages, which included £85 000 for pain and suffering, £627 730 for loss of future wages and pension rights and £397 304 for the cost of caring for her in the past and in the future.

> "All of a sudden everything was taken away from me. I couldn't do anything. I felt very isolated." *Margaret-Ann Reynard*

The restaurant owners contested the amount awarded but admitted liability for causing the salmonella infection. Mrs Reynard had hot and sour soup as a starter before sharing dishes of Cantonese beef, sweet and sour chicken and chicken in green pepper and black bean sauce with her fiancé. Mrs Reynard had egg-fried rice and her fiancé chose noodles.

The restaurant had been inspected by South Lanarkshire Council's environmental health officers in the summer of 2000 after 42 people contracted salmonella infection in the area. It was temporarily shut down then, and has since closed.

81 How much was awarded to Mrs Reynard? Do you think this was a suitable amount? Why?

82 What was the bacterium responsible for causing the food poisoning?

83 Which food do you think was responsible?

84 What were the effects on Mrs Reynard?

85 How many people suffered due to the effect of the food poisoning?

86 How long did it take for this to be proved through the courts? Is this an acceptable amount of time?

'Menu for bacteria!'

Starter:

- An ambient temperature of 25 degrees Centigrade.

Main:

- Water or high moisture content

Dessert:

- Nutrients available – however, not too much sugar or salt, e.g. jam or salted fish.

Optimum conditions for the growth of bacteria

Bacteria have preferred conditions for growth. Like us, they prefer warmth, nutrients and water. A high temperature (above 45 °C) kills bacteria. A cool temperature (below 5 °C) will only slow or temporarily stop the growth of bacteria. Even freezing (− 18 °C) does not kill them. They form spores, and when the food is defrosted the bacteria start to reproduce again.

> **87** What range of temperatures do bacteria like? Why is this a problem?

5.2 Avoiding contamination during food preparation

For the Unit 2 written examination you need to know:
- how food preparation areas are kept free of bacteria (personal hygiene, disinfectants, detergents, sterilisation, disposal of waste, control of pests, e.g. insects, mice);
- some examples of how the growth of bacteria is slowed down or stopped (refrigeration, freezing, heating, drying, salting, pickling).

Good general hygiene practices are important in a food business. The Food Safety Act requires all food companies, whether a large manufacturer or a small catering trailer, to train staff in how to prevent the cross-contamination of bacteria, and how to limit their growth.

Personal hygiene

Here are some simple hygiene precautions that can be taken at home or at work:
- **do** wash vegetables thoroughly to remove any microorganisms from the soil;
- **do** wash hands before handling food to prevent any microorganisms from getting on to food;
- **do** keep your food preparation area clean to reduce the risk of contaminating one food with the microorganisms from another food.

Personal hygiene is absolutely vital for anyone working in the food industry and coming into direct contact with food.

The Food Safety Act describes 10 golden hygiene rules. Check these on the Food Standards Agency website: www.food.gov.uk/foodindustry/hygiene

In addition to these basic precautions, workers in the food industry must wear a hat over their hair, and they must wear gloves if they handle food directly. These high standards of personal hygiene will reduce the spread of microorganisms from person to person, and also from people to the food being prepared.

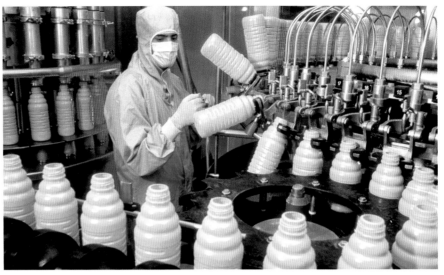

Figure 3.24 Personal hygiene is important in the food industry.

88 What is the simplest way of preventing infection from harmful microorganisms?

89 Give two examples of hazards in the food preparation area in Figure 3.25.

90 What problems are there in this kitchen?

Figure 3.25 A hygiene hot spot

Pests and waste control

Bacteria can be spread via hands, equipment and cloths, so it is important to keep all equipment clean and to dispose of waste food properly. Keep the dustbin lid clean too.

Do you have a part-time job working with food? If so, have you had proper training? If not, you should ask for training.

Insects or animals can cross-contaminate food by transferring bacteria from raw to cooked food. Food businesses must take reasonable precautions to prevent rats, mice, cockroaches and flying insects from entering food storage and preparation areas. Insect-proof screens on windows prevent flying insects entering a room, and gaps and holes must be filled in. Electric insect killers are useful, but chemical insecticides can't be used in food-preparation areas.

Sterilising and disinfecting

Personal hygiene is obviously important, but in addition disinfectants, antiseptics and sterilisation are used to kill bacteria and prevent them regrowing.

Equipment that comes into contact with food must be cleaned very carefully. The best way to ensure all the microorganisms have been removed or killed is to sterilise the equipment. Sterilisation involves either the use of gamma rays or heating the equipment to very high temperatures. Equipment to be treated by heating is placed in an **autoclave** and heated under pressure with steam to about 121 °C for 15 minutes. The high temperature kills the microorganisms – the equipment is then said to be sterile.

Autoclave
An industrial steriliser

Foods cooked in a pressure cooker are also effectively sterilised. In school laboratories, pressure cookers or autoclaves can be used to sterilise equipment, especially those used in microorganism experiments.

Some pieces of equipment in science laboratories, in hospitals, or in the food industry are not suitable for heating to high temperatures. This is often because they are made of plastic, which would melt. In these cases, gamma radiation is used to kill the microorganisms without the use of heat.

Figure 3.26 An industrial autoclave

Disinfectants

There are also some chemicals that can be used in the food industry and at home to ensure surfaces and equipment used for food preparation are thoroughly clean and do not have microorganisms on them. These chemicals are known as disinfectants. Disinfectants are bacteria-killing chemicals that are too strong to be used on human skin. They are used to clean floors and surfaces where food is prepared. It is important that food does not come into contact with disinfectants, as they are strong chemicals that we do not want to get into our mouths.

91 Why does equipment used in certain industries, like the food industry, need to be sterilised?

92 What are two different ways of sterilising equipment used in such industries?

Antiseptics and detergents

Antiseptics are chemicals that prevent bacterial growth. In the preparation of food, antiseptic soaps (these might be called antimicrobial) can be used to wash the hands and make sure they are free of most bacteria. Washing hands with plain detergent also helps remove bacteria from the hands and skin.

> **93** Disinfectants and antiseptics can both be used to help prevent infections from microorganisms. Describe how and why their uses are different from each other.

How can bacteria be slowed down or stopped?

Heat (sterilisation) kills bacteria. Refrigeration and freezing slow down bacterial growth, but do not stop it. So the following rules should be followed:

- **don't** refreeze frozen food that has thawed out, as microorganisms may now be growing in the food;
- **do** keep perishable food in the fridge, as the cold temperature restricts microorganisms' growth;
- **do** keep hot food hot, and cold food cold, until it is eaten, to reduce microorganisms multiplying at warm temperatures;
- **do** reheat food thoroughly to kill microorganisms that have already started to grow.

> **94** Why should cooked food be reheated thoroughly if it is not eaten straightaway?
>
> **95** Why does keeping perishable food in the fridge help prevent food poisoning?

Traditional methods using sugar, salt and vinegar are still used to preserve some foods. Salting and pickling both work by preventing the growth of microorganisms. This is why acidity regulators are used as food additives – low-acid foods are at more risk of food-poisoning bacteria.

Biltong
A South African dried meat

Drying food preserves it because most microorganisms can't live in a relatively dry environment. If you don't allow dried foods (such as **biltong**) to absorb moisture, they have a long shelf life.

5.3 Tests for detecting bacteria

You need to be able to:
- use aseptic techniques to swab areas to detect the presence of bacteria;
- make streak plates to identify the types of bacteria present;
- carry out tests on food products to determine the level of bacteria in the food;
- complete serial dilutions to make accurate counts of bacteria.

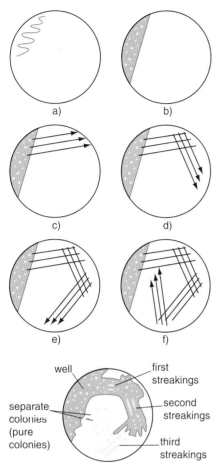

Figure 3.27 Producing a streak plate

Labels: a), b), c), d), e), f)

well — first streakings

separate colonies (pure colonies) — second streakings

third streakings

> **Aseptic technique**
> A technique used by microbiologists to protect themselves from harmful bacteria when handling microorganisms

Environmental health officers inspect local food business regularly. As part of their inspection they will take swabs to test work surfaces for bacterial contamination, and food samples to test for the presence of significant levels of harmful bacteria. There have been occasional product recalls (for example, chocolate bars from Cadburys) where tests have shown high levels of food-poisoning bacteria in processed food.

Detecting the presence of bacteria

You will do some practical work to practise **aseptic techniques**. Inspectors take a swab of something that must have bacteria on it (a work surface or a dirty plate) and seal it in a sterile bag until the sample can be taken to a laboratory. There they wipe the cotton bud over the surface of sterilised agar jelly in a Petri dish, and grow a culture or colony of bacteria. The agar contains nutrients that bacteria need to grow. The culture is incubated at a warm temperature so that large numbers of microorganisms can be grown.

A streak plate is used to spread the bacteria out over the surface of the agar. By the third or fourth streak, only a few bacteria cells are transferred. Round colonies grow around single bacteria. This makes it easier to identify the different bacteria present.

Figure 3.28 A Petri dish showing colonies of two different types of bacteria: *E. coli* (larger, reddish blobs) and *Staphylococcus aureus* (smaller, white blobs).

Practical Work – Investiating the effectiveness of different substances against bacteria

Procedure
1 Divide into four groups and choose a work station.
   - Group 1: investigate the effectiveness of disinfectants
   - Group 2: investigate the effectiveness of toothpastes
   - Group 3: investigate the effectiveness of different mouthwashes
   - Group 4: investigate the strength of antibiotic dosage on growth of bacteria
2 You have five sterile agar plates. Label the plates appropriately before you create them, so that you can leave them upright to dry. The labels should include the following:
   - Name
   - Date
   - Activity
   - Variable
3 First create a 'lawn' of *E. coli* on the agar plate. In groups, aseptically transfer a sample of *E. coli* onto a Petri dish and spread it along the surface of the agar using a flamed spreader dipped in alcohol.
4 After the bacteria have been streaked or spread out, it is very important that the Petri dishes are correctly labelled, taped up and allowed to dry.
5 Raise the lid of the Petri dish slightly. Using the sterilised metal core borer, aseptically cut a tiny well in the centre of the agar in the Petri dish. Replace the lid.
6 Next, aseptically place a small amount of **one** antibacterial product into the well on the agar plate:
   - Toothpaste
   - Mouthwash
   - Antibiotic disc
   - Disinfectant

Tape up the dishes and hand in the dishes to the teacher.

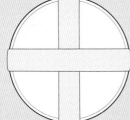

Petri dishes are usually sealed with two strips of adhesive tape from lid to base, not around the full circumference.

The Petri dishes containing agar are incubated at a fixed temperature – usually 37 °C, human body temperature, to detect pathogens, or 25 °C for bacteria from the environment. In schools, lower incubation temperatures, i.e. 25 °C, are used to discourage the growth of potential pathogens. Your technicians will monitor this.

When growing bacteria, it is usual to invert the Petri dishes to prevent condensation droplets from falling onto the surface of the agar. Petri dishes are often sealed with two strips of adhesive tape over the top and bottom of the dish, to prevent anyone who handles them from contamination by bacteria, which will multiply greatly. They are not taped all the way round to guard against the possibility of anaerobic organisms growing due to lack of air.

Cultures are usually examined after 24 hours' incubation, therefore, they must be refrigerated after the incubation period until the next lesson.

Bacteria on agar plates become visible as distinct circular colonies; each colony should represent an individual bacterial cell (or group) that has divided repeatedly – being kept in one place, the resulting cells have accumulated to form a visible patch.

Safety
Remember that any drips from a partially sealed Petri dish are potential sources of infection.

Safety
After use, bacterial cultures must be heat-sterilised before disposal. Hand all plates back to your teacher or technician – you don't know what bacteria you have grown, and their release into the atmosphere could damage your health.

Testing milk

Raw milk is tested regularly to see if the dairy has good hygiene. If you put a drop of milk on an agar plate, you may find that so many bacteria colonies grow, it would be difficult to count them. Using **serial dilutions** in sterilised liquids, the number of bacteria in a given amount of sample can be counted. The total bacteria count per ml in the original sample can be calculated.

Total bacterial count per ml = number of colonies × dilution factor

> **Serial dilution**
> A range of concentrations – a minimum of five dilutions, from concentrated to weak, will give the input variable

---

Practical Work – Investigating the shelf life of milk

You will find out the shelf life of pasteurised, full-fat milk stored at different temperatures. You do this by comparing the total number of bacteria every day for samples of milk stored at different temperatures.

Equipment
- Agar plates
- Bunsen burner
- Test tubes
- Measuring cylinder/pipettes, 10 cm³
- Distilled water
- Five individual pints of milk
- Ovens/water baths
- Refrigerator
- 1 cm³ pipettes
- Spreader (always flame to sterilise before and after use)
- Beaker of alcohol

Procedure
1 Store pints of milk at each of five different temperatures, for example 5, 15, 25, 35 and 45 °C. Each day, carry out the practical below. You may wish to divide up the work between the class and collate your results. (Hint – start with milk on its best-before date – this helps decrease the time needed to achieve some growth on the agar plates.)
2 Ensure all equipment has been sterilised.
3 Label six test tubes: 1/10, 1/100/ 1/1000, 1/10 000, 1/100 000, 1/1 000 000
4 Aseptically transfer 9 cm³ of sterile distilled water into each tube.
5 Aseptically transfer 1 cm³ of your milk sample into the first test tube, labelled 1/10.

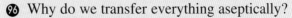

96 Why do we transfer everything aseptically?

- Mix thoroughly by agitating the tube between your finger and thumb.
- Aseptically pipette 1 cm^3 from tube 1 (labelled 1/10) into tube 2 (labelled 1/100) and again mix thoroughly.
- Repeat along the line of test tubes.
- Take six agar plates, invert and label them properly: name, date, milk and concentration (1/10 or 1/100 or 1/1000, etc.).

97 Why do we label them with name, date, milk, dilution and temperature?

- Aseptically transfer 0.1 cm^3 of the mixture from the test tube onto the appropriately labelled agar plate. For example, aseptically take 0.1 cm^3 of milk from the test tube labelled 1/1000, and place it on the agar plate labelled 1/1000. Use a spreader dipped in alcohol to spread the milk to form a 'lawn' of bacteria across the plate.
- Tape the plate.
- Repeat for all samples. Then wash your hands.
- Incubate the plates at 30 °C for 24 hours.

98 What function does the alcohol have?

99 Why must the spreader be flamed before it is used to create a lawn of bacteria?

100 Why do we tape up the plates?

101 Why is it important to wash your hands?

102 Why do we incubate the agar plates at 30 °C?

- The following day, count the colonies on each plate. If there are no colonies on any plate, continue to incubate until one plate shows colonies, and multiply the dilution factor by 10 to give an estimate of the number of bacteria in the milk sample.
- Record the number of bacteria you found, the dilution factor of the agar plate, and the temperature your milk sample was stored at.
- After a week, collate your results and dispose of the plates.

103 Who can dispose of the plates?

104 What factor are we looking at that may affect the shelf life?

105 What results are you expecting to see?

Safety

Hand all pates back to your teacher or technician.

6 Organic and intensive farming

Farmers produce food for profit, but have to consider the best methods to use in order to achieve a balance between profit and the quality of their products. Plants may be grown, and animals reared, in two contrasting types of farming.

In this topic you will learn about the:
- main differences between intensive and organic farming;
- advantages and disadvantages of each.

6.1 Intensive farming

For the Unit 2 written examination you need to:
- describe how intensive farming increases meat production by using controlled environments;
- understand that as crops grow they remove essential nutrients from the soils, and these nutrients need to be replaced;
- know that the plants need nitrates, phosphates, potassium and magnesium, which they obtain from soil, for healthy growth;
- describe how intensive farming increases crop yields by using artificial fertilisers, pesticides, herbicides and fungicides.

Agricultural scientists work with farmers to improve yields by controlling the conditions in which their animals and crops are grown. Rearing animals or growing crops in this way is known as intensive farming. A lot of money is spent when the farmer is setting up his intensive farm, but the cost of running the farm is usually much less than with other types of farming.

Intensive farming of animals

This involves keeping animals in purpose-built housing. Special machinery is used to control the amount of food and water, and the temperature. This is known as an automated system.

Advantages of intensive farming of animals:
- many animals are kept close together inside buildings, saving space;
- the biggest advantage is the low labour costs, as only a few people are needed to look after many animals.

Disadvantages of intensive farming of animals:
- the purpose-built housing costs the farmer a lot of money to build;
- often there are costs involved in setting up machinery to look after the animals;
- the farmer feeds his animals with expensive food so that they gain weight quickly.

Case Study – Battery chickens

In modern battery farms, just a few people can look after a million chickens. These people usually operate the machinery that feeds the chickens and collects the eggs. Keeping the chickens in cages means that they move around very little, putting almost all their energy into gaining weight and laying eggs.

The food supply can be regulated so that the chickens get just enough food of the correct type, but not too much. The temperature can also be controlled so that the chickens grow and lay eggs at the best possible rate. As these ideal conditions are easy for the farmer to maintain, he will soon be selling lots of eggs and plump chickens. This means it is usually worth the initial investments.

106 Do you feel this is an acceptable state for animals to be kept in? Explain your answer.

Intensive farming of plants

Plants, just like our bodies, require certain minerals for healthy growth. Nobody likes a limp lettuce. Plants take in these minerals from the soil through their roots. The most important minerals that plants need are nitrogen, phosphorus and potassium. Land used to produce crops must have these minerals added to the soil to stop them running out. Only by doing this can farmers make sure they are getting the best **yields**.

> **Yield**
> The amount of product made

Intensive farming uses artificial fertilisers to provide all the minerals that plants need to grow. Heavy rain can wash fertilisers from farmland into rivers. Today, large farms use satellite photographs and global positional system (GPS) tracking to map the fields. The readings tell you exactly what nutrients are present, and where in the fields. This allows the farmer to add exactly the correct amount of the right type of nutrient to the field. The aim is to prevent overload of nutrients into the food chain, and to prevent eutrophication of water in rivers. A cynic would also say the method was developed so that farmers do not have to waste money on fertilisers that are not used.

107 What are the causes of, and ways of preventing, eutrophication? How can this be cured?

Intensive farming also uses chemicals to kill unwanted organisms. These agrochemicals are pesticides, herbicides and fungicides. Pesticides (or insecticides) are sprayed onto plants to kill insect pests that eat the crops. Herbicides (weedkillers) are sprayed around the area of the crops to kill other plants that are growing in the wrong place (weeds). Fungicides can be applied to the seeds, roots or leaves of crops to destroy fungi that can cause diseases in plants.

Figure 3.29 A farmer spraying herbicide onto a field of wheat

> **108** Why do you think the number of wild flowers in the countryside has been decreasing?

Advantages of intensive farming of plants:
- artificial fertilisers are relatively cheap;
- artificial fertilisers, in the form of pellets or granules, can be spread over large areas of land quickly and easily by machinery;
- pesticides protect crops and increase their chances of survival.

Disadvantages of intensive farming of plants:
- the machinery needed to spread fertilisers and pesticides can be expensive;
- artificial fertilisers can be washed away by rain and cause problems in ponds and lakes – this problem (eutrophication) happens when nitrates get into the water, causing large growths of bacteria which suffocate fish;
- when crops are sprayed, they are covered with the chemical – it is important that crops are washed well before we eat them;
- chemicals may pass into the soil, and nearby plants and animals may also be contaminated – pesticides must be sprayed carefully, and in as small amounts as possible, to reduce the risk of affecting other organisms.

> **109** What properties do you think a chemical (pesticide, fungicide or herbicide) should have?

6.2 Organic farming

For the Unit 2 written examination you need to:
- describe how organic farming uses the alternative methods of natural fertilisers, natural pesticides and mechanical methods of eliminating weeds in crop production;
- describe how organic farming keeps animals under more natural conditions;
- compare the advantages and disadvantages of both types of farming.

In addition you should be able to assess the applications and implications of science when:
- comparing the advantages and disadvantages of both types of farming (food quality, cost, animal welfare, effect on environment).

Living organisms are made from organic compounds such as carbohydrates, fats and proteins. The elements in these organic compounds are constantly cycled between living organisms and their environment, as the living organisms respire, photosynthesise, excrete and die. This cycling of nutrients happens all the time in natural ecosystems. In autumn, when the leaves fall off the trees, the garden might look tidier if all the fallen leaves are collected. But they should be left to rot, decompose and return the nutrients back to the soil, to allow the buds to grow again in spring. So you now have a perfect excuse when you are asked to help in the garden!

Organic farming is so called because it uses methods and compounds that fit better with the natural environment. This is farming without the use of man-made chemicals.

Foods that are grown organically carry the Soil Association symbol. This symbol on food labels tells buyers that the food has been produced using organic farming methods, taking animal welfare and the environment into consideration. It also shows that the use of chemicals, such as artificial fertilisers and pesticides, has been avoided.

Organic farming of animals

Animal welfare is a major consideration in organic farming. Animals are reared in more natural conditions than in intensive farming.

Advantages of organic farming of animals:
- animals have more space each, and eat more natural foods, than those in intensive farming systems;
- animals are housed only during cold weather and spend the rest of their time outdoors, where they can graze and move around as much as they want;
- less money is spent on housing and food, and no chemicals need to be bought.

Figure 3.30 Organic pigs enjoy wide open spaces.

Disadvantages of organic farming of animals:
- animals take longer to gain weight under more natural conditions, so the farmer has to keep them for longer before he can sell them;
- the final product, for example beef, chicken or lamb, is more expensive to buy because the animals take longer to grow;
- animals require more looking after by more people, so labour costs are higher;
- animals have more space, so the cost of the land needed is higher – it is like housing a population of people in detached houses with gardens instead of in a block of flats.

Figure 3.31 'Intensive housing'

110 Why are more people needed to look after organically farmed animals?

111 Make a cost comparison of organic and non-organic meat.

Figure 3.32 Mechanical weeders are used in organic farming.

> **Biological control**
> Introducing a natural enemy to kill an insect pest

⑫ How is compost made?

⑬ What does 'biodegradable' mean?

⑭ Why do you think we are advised to wash our fruit and vegetables thoroughly before we eat them?

⑮ List some 'pests' that actually play a vital role in the ecosystem.

Organic farming of plants

In organic crop production, manures or composts are used to fertilise the soil. Manures are the waste products of animals, such as cow dung. Composts are made by allowing microorganisms to break down dead matter, such as vegetable peelings and fallen leaves.

Weeds are removed mechanically. This involves actually pulling them up, rather than adding chemicals to kill them.

Pests may be treated by **biological control**, for example where insect predators are used to kill insect pests. How crops are planted may also help to avoid pests. Planting certain crops together often means that one crop benefits the other. For example, one crop may attract natural predators that eat a pest of another crop.

A small number of naturally occurring chemicals are used as pesticides in organic farming. The best example of this is an insecticide called pyrethrum. This comes from dried flowers of the chrysanthemum plant. It is considered to be 100% natural and environmentally friendly. It kills insects but has no effect on animals, and breaks down naturally in the presence of sunlight (it is biodegradable), so it does not build up in the ecosystem.

Advantages of organic farming of plants:
- manure and composts are natural fertilisers and do not involve the use of man-made chemicals;
- crops are not sprayed with chemical pesticides;
- chemicals are not present on food or in the environment;
- there is no danger of contaminating food chains in the environment, or altering general natural patterns (for example by removing 'pests' that may actually play a vital role in the ecosystem).

Disadvantages of organic farming of plants:
- removal of weeds by hand or machine is time-consuming, and labour costs are high;
- foods tend to be more expensive to buy because of the increased labour costs;
- sometimes the appearance of the crops grown is less appealing.

Activity

Discuss the overall advantages and disadvantages of intensive versus organic farming – you may wish to compile the group's opinions in a table. Draw some conclusions about which type of farming you would prefer if you were:

a) a farmer
b) a consumer
c) an animal.

Unit 3 Investigation: Comparing the growth of differently treated barley seeds

In Unit 3 you have to complete at least one investigation for your portfolio. This investigation contributes 40% of the marks to the overall qualification. You will need to carry out an investigation, write a report and explain your findings. This investigation could be used as the basis for your portfolio for Unit 3.

Your report should:
- describe the purpose of the investigation;
- describe how the investigation is connected with food science;
- include a plan and risk assessment for the investigation;
- make conclusions from, and evaluate, the investigation;
- explain how a food scientist might use the results of the investigation.

Remember this is worth 40% of your overall marks.

Your investigation brief

1 Plan an investigation to find out the effects of growing food plants (barley seeds) under a variety of conditions. You could look at a variety of factors, including:
   - gamma radiation
   - amount of nutrients
   - different plant foods
   - storage temperature
   - amount of light
   - type of light
   - amount of water.
2 First, using the internet and other resources, carry out research on the significance of the plant you are growing. Where is it grown, and why? What uses does it have? What products does it make? What is its selling price?
3 Construct a plan of how you will carry out the investigation. The plan should be a series of well-ordered steps, and another scientist should be able to repeat the practical exactly as you plan to. Be careful to be very specific about timings, measurements and exactly what apparatus to use. Use diagrams to help you. Key phrases might include: 'Set up the apparatus as shown in the diagram.' The plan should be concise, but precise. It is always a good idea to ask someone else to read your plan to see if they understand what they would have to do – a parent or sibling, or even the friend sitting next to you. Ask them if they could carry out the practical – ask them to describe to you what *they* think you are asking them to do. This is an excellent way of ironing out any confusion within your plan.

4   As part of your plan, you must select appropriate apparatus from what you have available. Remember to make a note of any constraints you had to work under, and how you altered your initial plan to work around any problems. It is worth making a note of these as you go along – you, as scientists, will naturally work around problems without even realising you are doing it.

5   Complete a full risk assessment for your plan. The risk assessment must include chemicals and potential physical hazards, such as sharp scalpels. Explain how you will aim to prevent any accidents, but also what you would do if there were any mishaps.

6   Decide what to record. What data you obtain is extremely important. Decide which measurements you are going to take. Remember to think about the following questions.
    - How will you keep the test fair? Each practical must have only one control variable, yet you want to assess a variety of factors.
    - Will you repeat the tests? Do you have time to repeat after each test, or can you run several tests simultaneously?
    - How will you record your data? Design a results table before you start your practical, as part of your plan. Think about incorporating the use of ICT here, for example in the form of a spreadsheet.
    - Can you make any predictions about what might happen during the tests? What scientific knowledge do you have that supports your theory?

7   What to do with your data? At the end of the investigation you will have a lot of raw data. If you plan correctly, you will organise your data as you progress through the practical. Do not write all the measurements on little individual pieces of paper to collate at the end. Ensure you have a strong structure before you begin, or it is very easy to get into a muddle. You should be 100% sure which result applies to which measurement.
    Record your measurements in tables and graphs. Remember to label your axes very carefully. The horizontal x-axis is where you plot what you know (here, time in days); the y-axis is where you plot what you are measuring (here, height of plants in cm). Remember to give your graph a title: 'A graph to show …'. Points plotted should be in pencil, and placed carefully and discretely. Labels should be completed in blue/black ink.

8   Process the data. You must show an understanding of what the data are actually telling you. This is a good time to go back and read your initial plan and aim. Remind yourself of what were you hoping to find out. Can you answer your initial brief/question with the data you have achieved?
    Look at each of the factors you decided to investigate. Ask yourself the following questions.
    - Did the factor have any effect? (yes or no)
    - What was the effect?
    - Was it a large or small effect?

- How is this shown?
- How reliable is this result?
- What could you do to investigate this factor further?
- How could you make your data more reliable or valid?

9 What conclusions can you draw, using *only* your data? Do not write what you think should have happened – write about what your data are telling you.

10 Review your work. A review is where you look at:
- strengths within the plan
  - what worked well?
  - what problems did you solve?
  - where there were constraints, did you find good solutions to these problems?
  - what were these solutions?
- weaknesses within the plan
  - what problems did you encounter that you didn't manage to solve?
  - why were these problems?
  - how do you think they affected the results?
  - what would you like to do differently next time to improve the investigation? How do you think this would make the data more reliable?

11 Explain how your investigation could have some significance for farmers – could you use this information to decide about the seeds they should use, and in what conditions they should be grown? What would your recommendations to a farmer be, based on the evidence of your investigation?

12 References and bibliography – make a reading list to support your research. The reference list is what you have actually quoted from (copied), while the bibliography is what you have read to gain general knowledge and understanding, and then summarised in your own words.

❶ A new, healthy 'organic' café is opening up, and wants to ensure the foods on the menu are packed with as much nutrition as possible. The foods need to look appealing, but also to have lots of goodness. Describe a good preparation, cooking and eating process to preserve as much vitamin C as possible in carrots. *(6 marks)*

❷ The marketing department of a retailer is liaising with the product development team and discussing one of their product lines. A pasta ready meal is nearly ready to be launched into the market place. It is aimed at single working people, but also for busy families. The

Nutrition per 100 g

Protein = 8 g
Carbohydrate = 12 g
Calcium = 8 g
Vitamin = 1 g

Cooking instructions: remove all outer packaging and bake in the oven for 15 minutes

specification of the product is to be a quick, tasty, nutritious meal. The label gives its nutritional content. Prepare for the meeting by giving some thought to the following questions.

a) What information, missing from the cooking instructions, would be useful to add? *(1 mark)*

b) If the RDA for protein is 14 g, how much of the food product do they have to consume to achieve the full 100% RDA? *(2 marks)*

c) If the RDA for calcium is 11 g, what percentage does 100 g of the product provide? *(2 marks)*

d) If this packet costing £2.45 feeds one person, how much would it cost to feed a family of four? *(1 mark)*

e) Apart from giving essential information about the product, what other function do you think the label has? *(1 mark)*

❸ A reporter for a men's healthy eating magazine arranges an interview with a dietician at the doctor's surgery. The reporter wants to encourage readers to pursue a healthy diet. What answers should she get to her questions?

a) If you consume a very low-carbohydrate diet, such as the Atkins diet, where else can you get your energy? *(1 mark)*

b) Name two 'good' carbohydrates. *(2 marks)*

c) Name two good sources of fat. *(2 marks)*

d) Why is too much fat bad for you? On the other hand, why should you not consume a diet that contains no fat at all for a long time? *(4 marks)*

e) The reporter took down some answers, but they got into a muddle. Help her to unravel the facts in the table below by drawing an arrow from the food type to the function in the human body. *(6 marks)*

❹ On a doctor's surgery noticeboard, there is a poster giving warning signs of an unhealthy diet. There was a problem with the printing process – as the registered nurse, you have been asked to provide the relevant information. Copy and complete the table below and fill in the gaps. *(15 marks)*

Nutrient deficiency	Illness/ disease	Symptoms	Food sources
	Anaemia		
Calcium and vitamin D			
		Very sore teeth and gums	Citrus fruits
	Obesity	Overweight	
	Night blindness	Dryness in eyes	
		Poor healing of wounds	

Food type	Function in the body
Carbohydrate	Repairs body cells and helps you grow – male teenagers especially need this during adolescence
Fat	A concentrated store of energy, used for insulation, to improve the taste and texture of a meal, and to protect vital organs – can be a source of vitamins A, D, E and K
Protein	The main provider of energy – acts as a protein sparer
Vitamins and minerals	Like it or not – even those of us with muscles are mainly just this
Fibre	There are a lot of these, with different names and symbols (such as K)
Water	Life is very uncomfortable without this unofficial nutrient

❺ A product developer working for a major supermarket has been assigned the task of developing sausages. There are some new ranges in a competitor store, and you have to ensure your sausage looks and tastes better than any of the others.

a) Define the term 'additive' in your own words. *(1 mark)*

b) What could you use to increase the overall visual appearance of the sausage – what could you, as the manufacturer, do to it? *(1 mark)*

c) Additives are given a code. Which of the following letters does it begin with?
A   E   Z   *(1 mark)*

d) Once additives have been given this code they can be used in:
UK
Europe
World   *(1 mark)*

e) Name a natural colouring. *(1 mark)*

f) Your line manager is very against additives, yet your colleagues are for their use. In the table below (copy and complete), list advantages and disadvantages of using additives, to present to your line manager and colleagues and inform a balanced discussion. *(8 marks)*

Advantages of using additives	Disadvantages of using additives

g) If the consensus is not to use additives to increase the shelf life of the sausages, what other alternatives can you, as the product developer, think of? Again, give advantages and disadvantages of each process in order to present your ideas to a panel. *(9 marks)*

❻ Food labels have to give certain information by law. You need to design a new label for your newly developed sausages.

a) Research into the legal requirements for food labels according to the 1990 Act. To ensure your nutritional information is accurate, you first need to test whether the nutrient is present, using a qualitative test. Help the laboratory technician understand his task card. Unfortunately he spilt his cup of tea over it this morning, and some words are difficult to read.
Task card:
To test for the presence of protein, place a small sample in a test tube. Add $1\,cm^3$ of _____. If protein is present, the solution turns _____. To test for the presence of _____ you place the sample in a small beaker and add a few drops of iodine solution. The mixture turns _____ if the result is positive. To test for a reducing sugar such as glucose, dissolve a small amount of glucose in water first to _____ the powder. Add a few drops of _____ and place the tube into a _____. The colour turns brick _____ if a reducing sugar is present. *(8 marks)*

b) Design a food label for your sausages, satisfying all legal requirements. *(10 marks)*

❼ The Food Standards Agency (FSA) checks that food products match up to the claims on their labels and in their advertising. If you were employed by the FSA, and assigned to check Smarties®, how would you find out if the colours used actually match the label? Outline the experimental procedure you would use, including any health and safety precautions you need to take. *(7 marks)*

❽ A fresh batch of lard was collected from the cash-and-carry for the fish and chip shop. But on opening it, there was a rather metallic taste and a funny smell.

a) Name the chemical process that could have caused this strange taste and aroma. *(1 mark)*

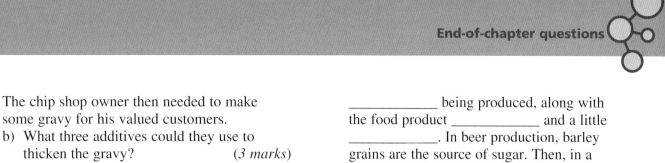

The chip shop owner then needed to make some gravy for his valued customers.

b) What three additives could they use to thicken the gravy? *(3 marks)*

9 Breweries make use of microorganisms in producing a variety of alcoholic beverages. Large and small breweries can produce lager, beer, wine, cider, and newer drinks termed 'Alco-pops'. This is a growing market that provides a wide range of careers.

a) Write the word and symbol equation for fermentation. *(3 marks)*

One of the main concerns for the brewing industry is the accusation that it is encouraging under-age, illegal drinking, especially with the production of 'Alco-pops'.

b) Why do you think alcohol is increasing in popularity? *(4 marks)*

In France it is illegal to give any alcohol to any children, even at home. If you do, you risk a prison sentence. France has a very low incidence of adolescent drinking.

c) Do you think this could be due to their strict laws? *(5 marks)*

One of the scientific jobs available in the brewing industry is to create the optimum conditions for the maximum rate of fermentation to occur. This makes it possible to produce the product more quickly, and increases the company's profit margin.

d) Design a test to assess which temperature is the best for the maximum rate of fermentation. *(2 marks)*

e) In preparing an introduction to a report for a scientific analyst at the brewery, use the words from the text box below to fill in the gaps. You may need to do a little bit of research to help answer the questions.

CARBON DIOXIDE   WORT
HOPS   ALCOHOL   SUGAR
ENERGY   RESPIRE   GERMINATE
MALTING   MASHING
MALTOSE

During fermentation, yeast uses _____ to r_____. This results in the gas _____ _____ being produced, along with the food product _____ and a little _____. In beer production, barley grains are the source of sugar. Then, in a process called m_____, the grains _____ and break down the starch into _____. This sugar is contained in a brown liquid called w_____. Finally, yeast is added to the _____ and the process of _____ begins. The flavour is created by the _____s. *(11 marks)*

f) If the sale of 'Alco-pops' did decrease, what other products could be made that use microorganisms in their manufacture? *(3 marks)*

10 The Department for Environment, Food and Rural Affairs (Defra) is a government department whose aim is to help create a sustainable food supply, supporting farmers, maintaining the ecosystem and putting in place systems to reduce risks of animal diseases, yet being ready to control them when they occur.

a) Defra has to consider two different types of farming – what are they? *(2 marks)*

b) Think about the costs and benefits of both types of farming. Copy and complete the table below. *(16 marks)*

Organic farming		Intensive farming	
Advantages	Costs	Advantages	Costs

c) Of the points in your table, which two do you think Defra would consider the most important? Why? *(2 marks)*

d) One ecosystem problem that Defra may discover is eutrophication. Define this term and state when it might occur. How do you prevent and cure it? *(8 marks)*

⑪ MRSA stands for methicillin-resistant (or multiple antibiotic-resistant) *Staphylococcus aureus*. On 25 April 2006, a ward at local hospital was closed following an outbreak of MRSA. Three patients on the colorectal ward contracted a resistant strain of the infection.

Sixteen patients were moved elsewhere in the hospital while the ward was cleaned, and the fire alarm system is also being updated. The hospital said it is confident the outbreak has been contained, and it was not found anywhere else on the ward.

a) Define 'aseptic techniques' Why do you think a hospital might use aseptic techniques? (*6 marks*)
b) Draw a line from the key word on the left-hand side of the column to the correct clue on the right-hand side.

Sterilisation	Before you have an injection, this is used on your skin
Immunisation	Helps keep surfaces and instruments free from bacteria and viruses (only partially successful)
Disinfectant	Kills some bacteria, but not viruses
Antiseptic	Elimination of all bacteria from a surface of piece of equipment
Antibiotic	Protects animals and humans from diseases

(*5 marks*)
c) How are hospitals limiting the number of cases of MRSA? What precautions are they taking? (*3 marks*)

⑫ No-one likes to suffer from food poisoning. The symptoms are not pleasant, and in some cases can be fatal and have serious consequences for numerous families. The 'Eat Safe' award has been in operation in Northern Ireland since June 2003, and has recently been extended to Scotland. It is administered by local council environmental health services in conjunction with the Food Standards Agency in both Scotland and Northern Ireland.

The idea of the 'Eat Safe' award is to encourage caterers to aim for food hygiene and food safety management standards above those required by law. It will also help consumers to make informed choices about where to eat out, by providing a recognisable sign of excellence in standards of food hygiene.

a) If you go to the doctor and they suspect food poisoning, who must the doctor notify? Why do you think this is? (*3 marks*)
b) Name the two types of bacteria that affect the food industry. (*2 marks*)
c) List some symptoms of food poisoning. (*4 marks*)
d) Draw a diagram of your kitchen, and highlight where you think there could be potential sources of bacteria that might be cross-contaminated onto food, which you might consume. How can you limit or control the contamination? (*6 marks*)
e) Bacteria prefer a temperature around:
A 5°C   B 15°C   C 25°C
D 35°C   E 45°C (*1 mark*)
f) All bacteria need oxygen to grow:
A Yes, or they are unable to reproduce and die.
B No, some are called anaerobic and can reproduce without any oxygen at all.
(*1 mark*)
g) If you were handling bacteria in industry in a microbiology laboratory, what health and safety practices would you observe?
(*2 marks*)
h) Do you think the 'Eat Safe' award is a good idea? Why? Should it be extended throughout the UK? (*1 mark*)

⑬ A local gymnasium is promoting special 'protein shakes' to weightlifters. It is thought that weightlifters need to drink these to gain body mass. Discuss the different functions of protein for people of different ages and activity levels. Justify whether the weightlifters should buy the protein drinks. (*5 marks*)

Chapter 4
Forensic science

Forensic science uses scientific techniques to identify and match substances or objects. Most of the work of the Forensic Science Service is for police forces investigating crimes, for example to analyse blood or bullets to identify a murder suspect, or to test powders suspected of being poisons or illegal drugs. Forensic scientists also work in other areas, for example to interpret archaeological remains, to investigate the cause of industrial accidents, or to show whether or not people are related. A wide variety of tests and methods are used to identify different substances or objects. The results often have to be used as evidence in a court of law, so accuracy and reliability are very important.

This chapter describes the science and techniques that you should learn to answer the forensic science questions for the Unit 2 examination. For your Unit 3 portfolio you may complete one investigation using the knowledge from this chapter. Some investigations and practical works are included throughout Chapter 4 that could contribute to your portfolio.

Chapter 4 is divided into four topics that represent the sequence of a forensic investigation:

1 Observing, recording and collecting evidence from a site or crime scene
2 Carrying out tests on evidence

3 Interpreting the results of tests using databases
4 Preparing a report and presenting it to a court of law

The following case study shows how this sequence is used in an investigation.

Case Study – Break-in

The manager of a bank arrived at work in the morning and found that the safe room had been broken into during the night. The manager contacted the police. The police told the manager not to touch anything at the crime scene.

When the police arrived they found the back door to the bank had been forced open and many strong boxes in the safe room were open. The police sealed off the crime scene and sent for the scenes-of-crime officers (SOCO).

The scenes-of-crime officers wore protective clothing so that they would not contaminate any of the evidence.

The first task of the scenes-of-crime officers was to take photographs of the crime scene that would provide a permanent record. The photographs of the crime scene could also be used as evidence in a court of law.

In most crimes, the person committing the crime will leave some physical evidence that can be used to link that person to the crime scene. This could be in the form of fingerprints.

The scenes-of-crime officers used a powder to dust the handle on the back door and the outside of the safes in an attempt to find any

---

fingerprints. The dusting revealed some fingerprints, which were then photographed. They then lifted the fingerprints using sticky tape, and placed the tape onto a white card for support. The officers labelled the card with a crime-scene number and recorded the position in which the fingerprints were found. The card was then placed in a sealed evidence bag. The evidence bag was labelled to include the details of the crime scene and the date of the crime.

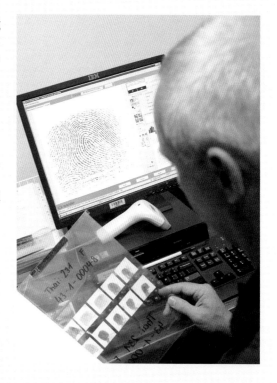

The fingerprints were taken to the forensic laboratory, where they were scanned into a computer. The scanned fingerprints were then entered into the Criminal Records Bureau's database, to see if they could find a match of the fingerprints with any of those held on the database.

The fingerprints matched a set of fingerprints held on the database. The technician then used the database to find the name and address of the person who had the same fingerprints as the sample obtained from the crime scene.

The police arrested this suspect and, as a result of further enquiries, the suspect was charged with the crime at the bank.

The forensic scientists produced a report on the fingerprint evidence, which was then presented as part of the evidence at the suspect's trial.

❶ Why would the police tell the manager not to touch anything at the crime scene?
❷ Why did the police officers seal off the crime scene?
❸ Why would the scenes-of-crime officers ask the staff working at the bank to have their fingerprints taken?

1 Observing, recording and collecting evidence from a site or crime scene

Contaminate
To add a substance by contact or mixing so that the original material is altered

As a scientific investigation, forensic work begins with the careful observation and recording of materials found at the site or crime scene. Before any laboratory testing can be carried out, samples need to be collected from the scene. Great care has to be taken to make sure samples are not **contaminated**, and that they are clearly labelled to make sure that are not misplaced.

This topic contains material you will need for the Unit 2 written examination and some techniques you may have to describe and carry out in your portfolio for Unit 3.

In this topic you will learn about methods of:
- avoiding contamination of evidence at a crime scene;
- recording evidence at a crime scene.

1.1 Avoiding contamination at a crime scene

For the Unit 2 written examination you need to be able to:
- describe how to avoid the contamination of evidence at a crime scene by restricting access, wearing protective clothing, using appropriate methods of sampling, storage and recording.

The first task of the police and scenes-of-crime officers is to seal off the crime scene so that no contamination of the evidence can happen. The officers need to make sure no unauthorised persons enter the crime scene, because they might remove or add evidence that could affect the outcome of the investigation.

If an unauthorised person enters a crime scene, they could remove vital evidence from the scene. This could include removing articles that might have fingerprints or bloodstains on them, or removing a weapon that might have been used in the crime.

Unreliable
Evidence that is uncertain because the forensic sample has been contaminated from another source

There are many examples of how crime scenes can be contaminated. Anyone entering the crime scene could leave their footprints, fingerprints, samples of fibres from their clothing or samples of hair from their body. These could be confused with evidence left when the crime was committed, making that evidence **unreliable**. It could lead to an innocent person becoming a suspect.

The crime scene is usually sealed off using crime-scene tape that restricts access to the scene. Only authorised people can enter the crime scene once it has been sealed off. In cases where the crime scene needs protecting from the weather, a tent is placed over the area.

Figure 4.1 Scenes-of-crime officers seal off the crime scene, wearing protective clothing to prevent contamination of evidence.

The scenes-of-crime officers always wear special clothing that prevents them contaminating any evidence. The clothing includes all-in-one body suits, gloves, overshoes, hairnets, masks and caps.

The protective clothing is designed to make sure the investigators do not transfer anything, such as their fingerprints, hairs or fibres from their clothing, to the crime scene.

❹ Why do scenes-of-crime officers wear a) gloves; b) overshoes?

Recording the site or crime scene

In most cases, a permanent record is made of the crime scene before anything can be disturbed or moved. This permanent record is important because it enables an accurate reconstruction of the crime scene at a later date, which may help in solving the crime. The permanent record of the crime scene can also be used as part of the evidence in a court of law.

It is especially important to make a permanent record when crime scenes are outdoors. There is always a possibility of the crime scene being affected by the weather. So a permanent record must be made as quickly as possible, before any evidence is contaminated or damaged by rain or wind. For example, if impressions of footprints or tyre prints are found at a crime scene, heavy rain could ruin the impressions.

Many different methods can be used to record the details of a crime scene. These include photography, sketches, video recording, or written details of the crime scene. It is also possible that the crime scene may be recorded using digital imaging techniques that can later provide a virtual tour of the area.

A useful website to visit to see a virtual tour of simulated crime scenes is:

www.crime-scene-vr.com

When photographs are taken at a crime scene, the scenes-of-crime officers will often place a ruler next to the evidence being photographed. This gives a scale to the developed photograph (see Figure 4.5, page 97).

Figure 4.2 Recording the crime scene

Recording evidence at the crime scene

The scenes-of-crime officers will always wear gloves when collecting evidence at a crime scene. The gloves make sure any fingerprints on the evidence are not contaminated with the fingerprints of the scenes of crime officers.

Once the samples from the crime scene have been collected, they are placed in an evidence bag. The bag is then sealed to make sure the evidence is not contaminated on its way to the laboratory. The label on the evidence bag gives information about the contents of the bag, the name of the scenes-of-crime officer who collected the evidence, and the date and place where the sample was collected. The location where the sample was taken is important, to make any identification and match **valid**. This means that when the sample is matched to a possible suspect, it is actually matching a sample from the exact, intended location.

> **Valid**
> Results answer the question being asked

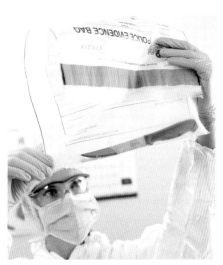

Figure 4.3 Evidence bags must be clearly labelled before storage.

The label may also give some information about the tests that the forensic technicians should carry out on the sample. For example, if a sample of a white powder is obtained from a crime scene, the label could include a request for the forensic technicians to test for drugs.

1.2 Collecting evidence from a crime scene

For the Unit 2 written examination you need to be able to describe:
- how to collect the following samples of forensic evidence: fingerprints, fibres and hairs, blood, broken glass or plastic, plant seeds and pollen, blood and soil;
- a suitable technique to reveal, lift and store a fingerprint left by a suspect at the scene of a crime;

- a suitable technique to make a permanent record of a mark or impression found at the scene of a crime;
- how to take appropriate samples from large quantities of materials.

You should also be able to use data, theories and explanations to:
- suggest why inappropriate collection or sampling techniques may lead to uncertainty about the validity and reliability of evidence.

Different methods are used to collect different types of sample.

Dusting for fingerprints

On some surfaces fingerprint impressions are easy to see, but in many cases the fingerprints have to be revealed before they can be collected.

> **Dusting**
> Using powder and a brush to detect and show up fingerprints on a surface

Dusting for prints is the oldest technique used in detecting (revealing) fingerprints. On most surfaces, fingerprints can be revealed by adding a very fine powder and then gently brushing away any excess powder with a fine brush. Most fingerprints are deposits of sweat and grease from the fingers or palms. The fine powder is absorbed by the moisture in the fingerprints and will appear as a pattern of lines.

The scenes-of-crime officers use different types of powder depending on the type of surface that is being examined for fingerprints. If the prints are on a light surface, then a dark powder such as carbon powder will be used to reveal any fingerprints. If the prints are on a dark surface, then a light-coloured powder such as aluminium powder will be used.

Figure 4.4 Dusting for prints

Lifting and storing fingerprints

Once the fingerprints have been revealed, there are two different methods of collecting them.

The fingerprint can be lifted using a clear adhesive tape (sticky tape) such as Sellotape®. Once the fingerprints have been lifted using adhesive tape, the tape is then placed on stiff card, which provides a support for the revealed fingerprints.

If aluminium powder is used to reveal the fingerprints, the adhesive tape with the fingerprints must be placed on a support card with a black background. If carbon powder is used to reveal the prints, the adhesive tape with the fingerprints is placed on a white support card. The support card with the fingerprints is then placed in an evidence bag.

Figure 4.5 Fingerprints revealed by dusting

> ❺ Why does the adhesive tape used to lift the fingerprints have to be clear tape?
>
> ❻ Why is the adhesive tape not placed on its own in the evidence bag?

Instead of using adhesive tape to lift revealed fingerprints, the scenes-of-crime officers can photograph them.

Whether the fingerprints are collected by adhesive tape or photographed, the prints will be scanned onto a computer so that they can be stored and compared with the fingerprint records held on the National Automated Fingerprint Identification System.

Collecting latent fingerprints

There are many cases where the prints cannot be seen. These prints are called latent fingerprints. In some cases it is easy to detect the fingerprints, and dusting will provide a good specimen for analysis. On **non-porous** surfaces such as glass, tile, metal or polished wood, dusting will make the prints visible.

Fingerprints on a **porous** surface can't be revealed using the dusting method. On a porous surface such as paper, cardboard or cloth, the sweat and grease in the prints is absorbed into the material.

Fortunately the sweat in most fingerprints contains **amino acids** and this allows the prints to be revealed. The surface of the cloth, cardboard or paper can be sprayed with **ninhydrin**, which reacts with the amino acids in the fingerprints. The reaction is speeded up by heating. The ninhydrin turns the fingerprint purple. The purple fingerprints can then be photographed.

Another method of revealing latent prints is to use super glue. Super glue vapour is blown over a surface where there may be latent prints. The super glue will condense on any fingerprints, revealing their pattern. The prints can then be photographed.

Great care must be taken when using ninhydrin and super glue, as they are both hazardous chemicals.

Collecting hair or fibre samples

In many cases, criminals will leave hairs from their head or bodies, or fibres from their clothing, at a crime scene. These hairs and fibres can be collected using tweezers or sticky tape, then placed in a sealed and labelled evidence bag.

Fibres are generally small, so the scenes-of-crime officers will often use a torch and a magnifying glass to locate hair or fibre samples.

It is also possible that fibres or hairs from the crime scene could be transferred onto the criminal's clothing. If the scenes-of-crime officers suspect this could have happened, they will take samples of fibres from carpets, curtains and furniture at the crime scene. As just a single fibre taken from a carpet and found on the suspect might be a contaminating fibre, the forensic officer will take several fibre samples. They also take

Non-porous
Describes surfaces that do not have holes, so fluids are not absorbed

Porous
Describes surfaces with small holes that can absorb fluids

Amino acids
The building blocks of proteins

Ninhydrin
A chemical used to detect amino acids, which can be used to detect fingerprints

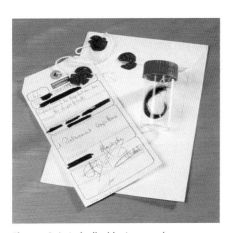

Figure 4.6 Labelled hair samples

Representative sample
A sample that is similar to the population from which it was drawn

random samples of all the fibres available. This ensures the sample is **representative**. The samples taken can then be matched to any evidence that might be obtained at a later time from a suspect.

Collecting blood samples

In the case of violent crimes, blood from the victim can be found at the crime scene or on the weapon that was used in the crime. If someone is attacked with a weapon, some of the blood could splash onto the attacker. Criminals may cut themselves and leave blood samples at the crime scene. Collecting blood samples from crime scenes can often lead to the identification of suspects.

Sterile
Free from microorganisms such as bacteria or fungi – if bacteria multiply in a blood sample, they decompose the blood and forensic tests will be unreliable

If the blood at the crime scene is still wet, it can be collected by swabbing with a **sterile** cotton bud or by smearing directly onto a sterile glass slide. The cotton bud or glass slide is then placed into a sealable tube before it is placed in an evidence bag.

❼ Why must the cotton bud or glass slide be sterile?

❽ Why is the cotton bud or glass slide placed in a tube before being placed in the evidence bag?

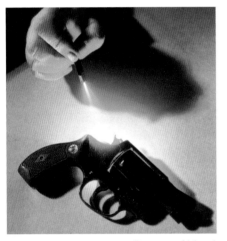

Figure 4.7 Detecting small traces of blood

If the blood has dried, it needs to be removed using a sharp implement such as a scalpel or a knife. The scalpel or knife is used to scrape some of the blood from the dried blood sample. Dried blood can also be collected using a damp, sterile cotton bud. The blood sample is then placed in a labelled evidence bag.

In some crimes, criminals may clean up the crime scene in an attempt to remove any evidence that could be used to link them with the crime. However, it is not easy to remove all traces of blood from a crime scene.

Luminol
A chemical used to detect blood

Scenes-of-crimes officers can find small traces of blood using a chemical called **luminol**. The crime scene is blacked out so there is no natural light, and then the crime scene is sprayed with luminol from an aerosol.

The luminol reacts with any blood present and produces a blue-green fluorescence (glow) under ultraviolet light. Luminol is very sensitive and will produce a blue-green glow with the smallest spot of blood. The position of any blood spots can then be recorded using a video camera or by taking photographs.

Luminol is also used to find small droplets of blood that form a splatter pattern in violent crimes. The blood splatter pattern can be used to provide information about the violence and direction of an attack.

Collecting samples of broken glass

The broken glass could be from a broken window, drinking glasses, glass bottles or spectacles. In the case of road traffic accidents, broken glass from car windows, headlights or sidelights might be left at the scene of the accident.

If there is broken glass at a crime scene, there is always a chance that some of the glass fragments will be on a suspect's clothing or stuck in the sole of the suspect's footwear. There is also a possibility that some fragments of broken glass could be in a suspect's car.

Samples of broken glass from a crime scene can be collected using tweezers or sticky tape. As with fibres, if there is a large amount of material the forensic officers must take several representative samples. On some occasions a small vacuum cleaner is used to collect small samples of broken glass. The samples would then be placed in a labelled evidence bag.

Collecting seeds and pollen

If a crime has been committed outdoors, there is a possibility that there will be plant seeds or flower **pollen** that can be used to link a suspect to the crime. Plant seeds are visible to the naked eye and can be collected using tweezers or sticky tape and then placed in a labelled evidence bag. A paper bag is used for plant material, as plastic bags would lead to decay.

Pollen grains are so small that it is difficult to see them with the naked eye. Samples of pollen must be collected using sticky tape. The tape is then placed on stiff card for support, which is then placed in a labelled evidence bag.

Pollen
The minute grains produced by the male part of flowers to fertilise plant egg cells

9 What would a scenes-of-crime officer use to find very small pieces of glass at a crime scene?

10 Why is not possible to collect pollen samples with tweezers?

Collecting soil samples

Samples of soil recovered from a crime scene can also be used to link a suspect to the crime scene. Some of the soil from the crime scene may be on the suspect's footwear, on the tyres of the suspect's vehicle, or even inside the car.

Whenever the scenes-of-crime officers make a cast impression of footwear or tyre marks, they will also take a sample of soil from the crime scene for analysis. This soil can then be chemically analysed for comparison with any soil obtained from a possible suspect. Soil samples can be collected using a small trowel or a spatula.

Recording marks and impressions at a crime scene

Criminals may leave footprints or tyre marks from the vehicle they used in committing the crime. When criminals use tools to force open a window or door, the tool (for example a screwdriver or crowbar) may leave a mark in the paint or woodwork. The tool used can be matched to the marks made in the paint or woodwork.

Marks and impressions left at the scene of a crime may be recorded using plaster of Paris or Plasticine, or by taking photographs of the impressions. The marks or impressions made at a crime scene can be compared with tools, tyres and the soles of shoes owned by a suspect.

Footprints and tyre marks left in soft surfaces, such as soil or grass, can be collected by making a cast of the impression left by footwear or a vehicle tyre. In most cases the scenes-of-crime officers will take photographs of the marks before they make a plaster cast impression of them.

Figure 4.8 Marks and impressions can be analysed by forensic scientists.

To make a cast of an impression:

1

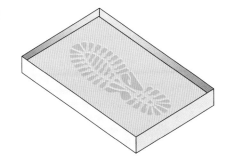

A protective border is made round the impression. The border can be made with stiff cardboard or plastic. If the soil is very dry, it can be sprayed with hairspray so that the shape of the impression is not spoiled when the wet plaster is added.

2

Plaster of Paris is mixed with water to form a smooth mixture that will flow easily.

3

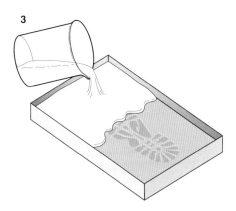

The plaster of Paris mixture is very carefully poured into the impression so that the pattern of the impression is not altered.

4

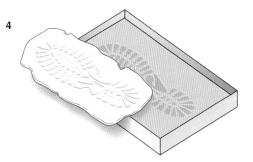

When the plaster mix has dried (hardened), the plaster cast is removed. The cast is then labelled with the crime scene number and date.

Figure 4.9 Making a plaster cast of an impression

Figure 4.10 Recording footprints on a smooth surface

Footprint marks may also be made on smooth surfaces. This can happen when the soles of the footwear are damp or are covered in mud or damp soil. When somebody wearing such footwear walks across a smooth surface, they will leave prints from the footwear on the surface. (It is very similar to leaving fingerprints on smooth surfaces.) Footprints can also be left when someone walks on a smooth surface that has a layer of dust on it.

These footprints are recorded using photography. The scenes-of-crime officers will place a ruler by the side of the footprints and then photograph them.

> ❶ Why will the scenes-of-crime officers use a ruler when taking photographs of footprints or tyre impressions?

Impression marks made by tools used to break open doors or windows can be photographed, or Plasticine can be used to make a copy of the mark.

Table 4.1 summarises the different methods used to collect samples, and some forensic tests that could be carried out on them. The tests are described in the next topic.

Figure 4.11 Forced door at burglary scene that could be examined for impression marks

Sample	Collection method	Tests
Fibre or hair	Tweezers or sticky tape	Compare using microscope
Fingerprint	Revealed by dusting with powder, then photographing or lifting the fingerprint with sticky tape	Compare with records on database
Soil	Small trowel or spatula	Chemical tests
Footprint/tyre mark	Plaster cast	Compare with suspect's footwear/vehicle tyres
Tool mark/impression	Plasticine	Compare with tools obtained from suspect
Blood	Wet blood can be smeared onto a glass slide Dry blood can be scraped off with a scalpel or sterile, damp cotton wool bud	Blood typing, blood grouping, DNA profiling
Broken glass	Tweezers, sticky tape or a small vacuum cleaner	Refractive index
Plant seeds	Tweezers, sticky tape	Examination under a microscope
Pollen	Sticky tape	Examination using electron microscope

Table 4.1 Sampling methods and forensic tests

2 Carrying out tests on evidence

All tests carried out by forensic scientists involve matching evidence obtained from a crime scene with materials or substances that have already been identified. Forensic scientists use many types of test to help link evidence collected from a crime to a possible suspect. These tests are based on:
- chemical techniques;
- biological techniques;
- physical techniques.

Many of these tests can be carried out in the school or college laboratory, as well as with more powerful equipment available in forensic laboratories.

This topic contains material you will need for the Unit 2 written examination, and some techniques you may have to describe and carry out in your investigation for Unit 3.

In this topic you will learn about:
- chemical knowledge used by forensic scientists, including:
  - different types of chemical bonding
  - writing formulae of some chemical compounds
  - the relationship between physical properties of compounds and their structure and bonding;
- chemical tests used by forensic scientists;
- biological tests used by forensic scientists;
- physical tests used by forensic scientists.

2.1 Chemical knowledge needed by forensic scientists

For the Unit 2 written examination you need to be able to:
- describe the structure of ionic compounds as consisting of a giant lattice held together by strong forces of attraction between positively charged and negatively charged ions (e.g. sodium chloride);
- explain why ionic compounds have high melting points;
- recall that many substances that are obtained from living materials are organic compounds with covalent bonding;
- name some simple covalent compounds, given their formulae; and state the formula, given the name of the compound (carbon dioxide, CO_2; water, H_2O; ethanol, C_2H_5OH; glucose, $C_6H_{12}O_6$);
- understand that, although the covalent bonds between the atoms in a molecule are strong, the forces between the molecules are weak;
- explain why covalent compounds have low melting points and boiling points.

You should also be able to use data, theories and explanations to:
- state whether an ionic compound is soluble in water;
- write the formula for an ionic compound.

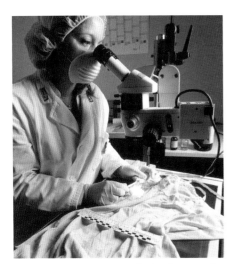

Figure 4.12 Forensic analysis of material taken from a crime scene

The melting point and boiling point of a substance, and whether it can be dissolved in water, are unique to that substance. These characteristic properties of a substance enable it to be identified.

The physical properties of a substance, such as its melting point, depend on how the particles in a substance are arranged (structure) and how they are held together (bonding).

All atoms contain three elementary particles: protons, neutrons and electrons. The protons and neutrons are found in the nucleus of the atom. The electrons are in energy levels (shells) outside the nucleus.

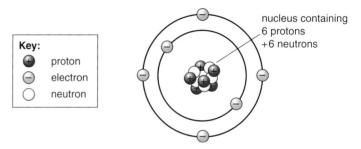

Key:
⊕ proton
⊖ electron
○ neutron

nucleus containing 6 protons +6 neutrons

Figure 4.13 An atom is mostly empty space – negatively charged electrons surround a small, positively charged nucleus.

When atoms combine in chemical reactions to form compounds, chemical **bonds** are formed. Bonding involves the **outer electrons** in the atoms. There are two types of bonding: ionic and covalent.

Ionic bonding

In **ionic bonding**, electrons are transferred between atoms. Ionic compounds are formed when atoms transfer electrons to form **ions** that carry a charge. The atoms that lose electrons form positive ions, and the atoms that gain electrons form negative ions.

The simplest example is sodium chloride. The sodium atoms each lose an electron to form sodium ions with a single positive charge, Na^+, and the chlorine atoms each gain an electron to form chloride ions with a single negative charge, Cl^-.

Bonds
Chemical bonds between atoms are the forces that hold them together in compounds

Outer electrons
Electrons in the outer shell of an atom, furthest from the nucleus

Ionic bonding
Formed by the electrical attraction between oppositely charged ions

Ion
A charged particle, formed when electrons are added or removed

⑫ Aluminium atoms forms Al^{3+} ions. How many electrons does an aluminium atom lose to form an Al^{3+} ion?

⑬ Explain how oxygen atoms form O^{2-} ions.

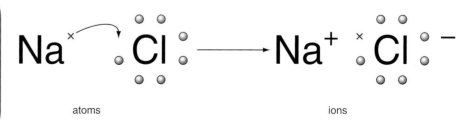

atoms

ions

Figure 4.14 Formation of ions from the atoms of sodium and chlorine

Ionic compounds form giant three-dimensional **lattices**. In sodium chloride, each sodium ion is surrounded by six chloride ions; each chloride ion is surrounded by six sodium ions.

Lattice
The regular arrangement of particles in a three-dimensional structure

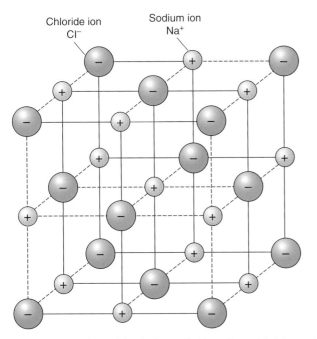

Figure 4.15 Sodium chloride lattice (left); sodium chloride crystals (right)

Soluble
Can be dissolved in a solvent, e.g. water

Solution
A solid, liquid or gas dissolved in a solvent

Covalent bonding
The sharing of a pair of electrons between two atoms to form a molecule

Molecule
A particle containing two or more atoms joined by covalent bonds

Ionic bonding is the strong forces of attraction between oppositely charged ions. A lot of energy is needed to overcome these forces and so break down the giant lattice. This means that ionic compounds are solids with high melting points.

Most simple ionic compounds are **soluble** in water. This is because the water molecule has slightly charged parts, which form a slight attractive force to the positive and negative ions in the solid. If these forces are large enough they can break the ionic bonds. The ions pass into the water, making a **solution**.

Covalent bonding

In **covalent bonding**, pairs of electrons are shared between atoms. Covalent compounds form when atoms share pairs of electrons: each atom contributes one of the electrons to the shared electron pair. When atoms combine by sharing electrons, **molecules** are formed.

Covalent bonds are formed when non-metals react with each other. Living materials contain mainly carbon compounds (organic compounds) such as glucose, wood or natural fibres. These organic compounds all have covalent bonding.

> **Intermolecular forces**
> The forces between molecules in a solid or liquid
>
> **Insoluble**
> Cannot be dissolved in water

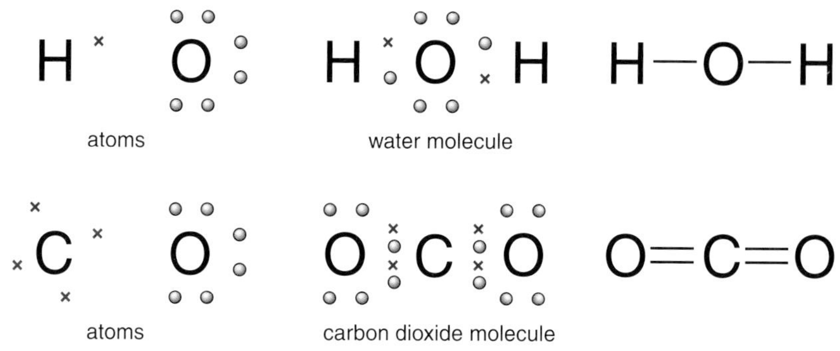

H $\overset{\times}{}$ $\overset{\circ\ \circ}{\underset{\circ\ \circ}{O\ \circ}}$ H $\overset{\circ\ \circ}{\underset{\circ\ \circ}{\times O \times}}$ H   H—O—H

atoms   water molecule

$\overset{\times}{\underset{\times}{\times C \times}}$ $\overset{\circ\ \circ}{\underset{\circ\ \circ}{O\ \circ}}$ $\overset{\circ\ \circ}{\underset{\circ\ \circ}{O}}\overset{\times}{\underset{\times}{C}}\overset{\circ\ \circ}{\underset{\circ\ \circ}{O}}$ O=C=O

atoms   carbon dioxide molecule

Figure 4.16 Formation of H_2O and CO_2

Covalent bonds are strong – but the forces of attraction between separate molecules are weak. These weak **intermolecular forces** (between molecules) are easily broken. This means it does not require very much energy to overcome the intermolecular forces and separate the molecules from each other. As a result, simple covalent compounds have low melting points and boiling points. This means that many simple covalent compounds will be liquids or gases at room temperature. Most covalent compounds are **insoluble** in water.

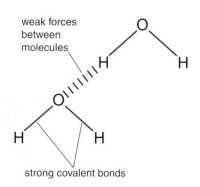

Figure 4.17 Intermolecular forces between two water molecules

Formula of a compound

The formula of a compound tells us which elements are in the compound, and how many atoms of each element there are in it.

The formula of simple ionic compounds can be worked out using the charges on the ions. An ionic compound does not have an overall charge and therefore the charges on the ions present in the compound must cancel out. This is best shown by examples.

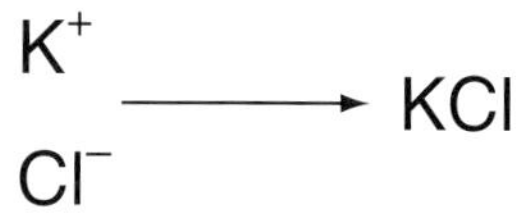

$$K^+ \\ \longrightarrow KCl \\ Cl^-$$

Figure 4.18 Potassium chloride

Potassium chloride contains K^+ ions and Cl^- ions. As these have equal but opposite charges, the compound will have equal quantities of the two different ions. This gives the formula KCl (Figure 4.18).

$$Na^+ Na^+ \longrightarrow Na_2O \\ O^{2-}$$

Figure 4.19 Sodium oxide

Sodium oxide contains Na^+ ions and O^{2-} ions. The charge on the oxide ions is twice that on the sodium ions. This means that there will be two Na^+ ions for every O^{2-} ion. This gives the formula Na_2O (Figure 4.19).

$$Mg^{2+} \\ \longrightarrow MgO \\ O^{2-}$$

Figure 4.20 Magnesium oxide

Magnesium oxide contains Mg^{2+} ions and O^{2-} ions. These ions have equal but opposite charges, and the compound will have equal quantities of the two different ions. This gives the formula MgO (Figure 4.20).

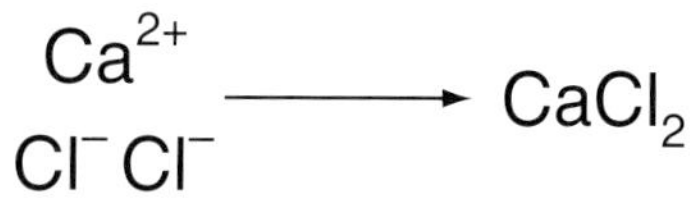

$$Ca^{2+} \\ \longrightarrow CaCl_2 \\ Cl^- Cl^-$$

Figure 4.21 Calcium chloride

Calcium chloride contains Ca^{2+} and Cl^- ions. The charge on the Ca^{2+} ion is twice that on the Cl^- ion. This means there will be one Ca^{2+} ion for every two Cl^- ions. This gives the formula $CaCl_2$ (Figure 4.21).

You will need to show that you can write the formula of an ionic compound using information on the ions present in the compound.

14 Using the following ions, write the formula for the compounds given:

Cu^{2+} Mg^{2+} Al^{3+} Cl^- O^{2-}

Copper oxide

Magnesium chloride

Aluminium oxide

It is more difficult working out the formula of a covalent compound. You need to learn the name and formula of the following covalent compounds:

Water H_2O

Carbon dioxide CO_2

15 Name the elements present in glucose.

Ethanol C_2H_5OH

Glucose $C_6H_{12}O_6$

Feature	Ionic	Covalent
Formation	Formed by transfer of electrons	Formed by sharing pairs of electrons
Contain	Ions	Molecules
Melting point/boiling point	High	Low
Solubility in water	Most dissolve in water	Most are insoluble in water

Table 4.2 Summary of ionic and covalent compounds

2.2 Some chemical tests used by forensic scientists

For the Unit 2 written examination you need to be able to:
- describe how to detect the presence of Na^+, K^+, Ca^{2+} and Cu^{2+} ions using flame tests;
- describe how to test the solubility of a compound in water;
- describe how to obtain a clear solution for use in further tests;
- describe the use of universal indicator paper to measure the pH of a solution;
- describe the use of precipitation reactions to detect the presence of Ca^{2+}, Cu^{2+}, Fe^{2+}, Fe^{3+}, Pb^{2+}, Cl^- and SO_4^{2-} ions;
- describe the reaction of CO_3^{2-} ions with dilute acid;
- describe the test for carbon dioxide using limewater;

- describe the test for ethanol using acidified potassium dichromate solution and outline the use of this reaction in the original breathalyser;
- describe the test for glucose using Benedict's solution;
- describe the separation of coloured mixtures using thin-layer and paper chromatography with both water and **non-aqueous solvents**;
- explain why different colours in a mixture are carried different distances by the solvent, and how this observation can be used to match the mixture with known samples or identify the substances present in the mixture;
- suggest why instrumental techniques provide more precise and reliable evidence than that obtained from simple laboratory experiments;
- suggest ways to improve the accuracy and reliability of the evidence being collected.

You should also be able to use data, theories and explanations to:
- name the product of a precipitation reaction;
- draw conclusions about the identity of substances when given the results of a series of chemical tests.

Forensic scientists can test for many types of substance using chemical techniques. You need to know about:
- the different types of chemical testing;
- the information obtained from the chemical tests;
- how the results of the tests are used by the forensic services.

Some examples of the more common samples include:
- drug samples to see which chemicals have been added to the drugs obtained from a suspect;
- soil samples from crime scenes to compare with samples taken from the shoes or car tyres of suspects;
- blood or urine samples to find the amount of alcohol present.

Simple chemical tests can be used to help identify a large range of compounds that may be present in a sample obtained from a crime scene. This is **qualitative analysis**. Qualitative tests identify the different substances present in a sample. The results can then be used to link a suspect to a crime scene.

These must not be confused with **quantitative analysis**. Quantitative tests tell us how much there is of a substance. (Quantitative comes from the word 'quantity'.)

Flame tests

Spectacular firework displays rely on the fireworks producing a large range of different colours. These colours are produced by adding small amounts of different metal salts to gunpowder. When the gunpowder ignites, it releases a lot of heat energy that makes the metal ions give off light of different colours. We can use this idea in **flame tests**.

Non-aqueous solvents
Solvents other than water

Qualitative analysis
Procedure to determine the identity of a substance using a series of simple chemical tests

Quantitative analysis
Procedure to determine the quantity of a substance

Flame test
A simple test to detect metal ions using a wire above a Bunsen burner flame – different metal ions produce different flame colours

Figure 4.22 What metal ion is present in this flame test?

Safety

Wear goggles.

Practical Work – How to carry out a flame test

1 Light a Bunsen burner and open the air hole so that the flame burns blue.
2 The nichrome wire is first cleaned by dipping the wire into concentrated hydrochloric acid and then holding it in the side of the Bunsen flame.
3 Once it has been cleaned, the wire is dipped into acid again, and then into the compound being tested.
4 The wire holding the sample is then held in the side of the Bunsen flame.

Care: concentrated hydrochloric acid is corrosive.

An alternative method is to use a wooden splint (or spill) instead of a nichrome wire. The wooden splint is wetted with water before it is used. This stops the splint burning in the flame, and also makes it easier for the sample to stick to the splint.

16 Why is the nichrome wire cleaned in the flame before it is used in a flame test?

You need to know the flame test colours for the following metal ions (Table 4.3).

Metal ion	Colour of flame
Sodium (Na^+)	Yellow
Potassium (K^+)	Lilac
Calcium (Ca^{2+})	Brick-red
Copper (Cu^{2+})	Green

Table 4.3 Flame test colours

Solubility
How much of a soluble solid can dissolve in a solvent

Solvent
A substance (usually a liquid) that dissolves another substance to form a solution

Testing solubility

One of the first tests that forensic technicians would perform on a sample obtained from a crime scene is **solubility**. The technicians would find out whether the sample is soluble in water or is soluble in an organic **solvent**.

Practical Work – How to test for solubility

To test the solubility of a sample you would add a small amount of the sample to some water in a beaker and see if the sample dissolves. The water should be stirred or warmed to speed up the process. Solubility can be measured in grams of solute per 100 g of water, at a certain temperature.

The same method would be used to test if the sample is soluble in organic solvents.

Some samples may be a mixture of two or more substances – it is important to separate these substances before they are tested. This is because the results of the tests can interfere with each other. For example, copper ions and calcium ions give different flame test colours. If a mixture contained both copper and calcium ions, the colours in the flame test would interfere with each other and you would not be able to identify either the copper ions or the calcium ions in the sample.

17 What is a mixture?

Filtration
Separation of a solid from a liquid using filter paper

One simple separation technique involves **filtration**. This can be used to separate a soluble substance from an insoluble substance.

Practical Work – How to separate a mixture by filtration

Filtration involves adding an excess of water to make sure all the soluble compound dissolves. Stirring the mixture thoroughly helps to speed up the process.

The mixture is then passed through filter paper. The insoluble substance (residue) remains in the filter paper and the dissolved substance (filtrate) passes through the filter paper.

The residue is then rinsed with water and dried. If the soluble substance is needed in solid form, it can be recovered from the filtrate by evaporation to dryness.

18 Suggest another method to speed up the dissolving process.
19 Why is the residue rinsed with water?

Water is only one example of a solvent that can be used to separate a soluble substance from an insoluble substance. Organic solvents, such as alcohol or hexane, could be used.

Testing the pH of a sample

One of the simplest tests that technicians carry out is to find out whether a sample contains an acid or an alkali.

Practical Work – How to test for pH

1 First, the sample must be dissolved in water.
2 Litmus paper is then dipped into the solution.
3 If the litmus paper turns from blue to red, the sample contains an acid; if the litmus paper turns from red to blue, the sample contains an alkali.

Litmus paper only shows if a sample contains an acid or an alkali. More information can be found by using universal indicator to measure the pH of the dissolved sample.

pH is a measure of acidity, and is used to find how acidic or alkaline a substance is.

The pH scale goes from 0 (a very strong acid) to 14 (a very strong alkali).

To find the pH of a solution, the universal indicator paper is dipped in the solution and the colour of the universal indicator is then compared with a colour chart to find the pH.

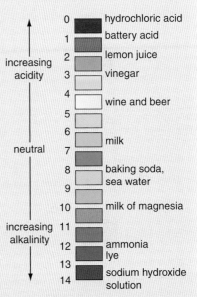

Figure 4.23 Universal indicator paper is used to measure the pH of a solution.

A more accurate way of measuring pH is to use a pH meter. A pH meter measures the pH of a solution electronically, and the pH is displayed on the meter.

Before using a pH meter, it must be **calibrated** by placing the probe of the pH meter in a buffer solution with a known pH, then the pH meter is adjusted so that its pH is the same as that of the buffer solution. For very accurate work, the pH probe is placed in two or three solutions of different pH, and the pH value on the meter is recorded. The results are used to draw a calibration curve for the meter.

Calibrate
Test a measuring device to check its accuracy

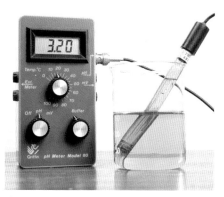

Figure 4.24 A pH meter

> **Precipitation reaction**
> A reaction that produces a solid from solutions – the solid produced is called a precipitate

Figure 4.25 Two solutions can react to produce an insoluble precipitate.

The pH test is often used in comparing soil samples. Water is added to a soil sample and the mixture is stirred thoroughly. The mixture is then filtered and the pH meter is used to find the pH of the filtrate.

> ❷⓿ The pH of a solution is 4. What does this tell you about the solution?

Using precipitation reactions to test for ions

Some metal ions (positive ions) and some negative ions can be identified by simple **precipitation reactions**. Precipitation reactions involve mixing two soluble compounds in solution to form an insoluble solid compound, which appears as a precipitate.

If the sample is in solid form, it must be dissolved in water before carrying out a precipitation test. If dissolving the sample in water does not result in a clear solution, this could interfere with precipitation tests. If this happens, the solution should be filtered. This should produce a clear solution.

Many metal ions can be detected by adding sodium hydroxide solution to a solution containing the metal ion. Different metal ions produce a different coloured precipitate, so this identifies the metal substance present in the sample.

Examples

$$\begin{array}{ccccc}
\text{copper(II)} & & \text{sodium} & & \text{copper(II)} & & \text{sodium} \\
\text{chloride} & + & \text{hydroxide} & \rightarrow & \text{hydroxide} & + & \text{chloride}
\end{array}$$

$$CuCl_2(aq) + 2NaOH(aq) \rightarrow Cu(OH)_2(s) + 2NaCl(aq)$$

Copper chloride is a blue powder that is soluble in water. The reaction produces copper hydroxide, which is insoluble and forms a blue precipitate.

$$\begin{array}{ccccc}
\text{iron(II)} & & \text{sodium} & & \text{iron(II)} & & \text{sodium} \\
\text{chloride} & + & \text{hydroxide} & \rightarrow & \text{hydroxide} & + & \text{chloride}
\end{array}$$

$$FeCl_2(aq) + 2NaOH(aq) \rightarrow Fe(OH)_2(s) + 2NaCl(aq)$$

Iron(II) chloride is a green powder that is soluble in water. The reaction produces iron(II) hydroxide, which is insoluble and forms a green precipitate.

Practical Work – How to test for metal ions

1 Place about 1 cm depth of a test solution into a test tube.
2 Add a few drops of dilute sodium hydroxide solution.
3 If there is a metal ion in the test solution, a precipitate will form. Note the colour of the precipitate.
4 Then add more sodium hydroxide to see if the precipitate formed will dissolve in excess sodium hydroxide.

Care: dilute sodium hydroxide is an irritant.

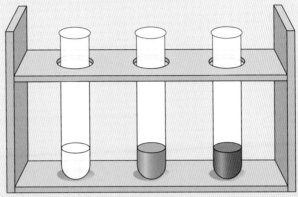

Figure 4.26 If there is a metal ion in the test solution, a precipitate will form.

You need to know the colours and names of the precipitates formed by adding sodium hydroxide to the metal ions listed in Table 4.4.

Metal ion	Colour of precipitate formed with sodium hydroxide solution	Name of precipitate
Calcium (Ca^{2+})	White	Calcium hydroxide
Copper (Cu^{2+})	Blue	Copper hydroxide
Iron(II) (Fe^{2+})	Green	Iron(II) hydroxide
Iron(III) (Fe^{3+})	Orange/brown	Iron(III) hydroxide
Lead (Pb^{2+})	White	Lead hydroxide

Table 4.4 Precipitate formed by various metals with sodium hydroxide

Both calcium and lead ions give a white precipitate with sodium hydroxide, but if excess sodium hydroxide is added, the precipitate formed with lead ions will dissolve to give a colourless solution.

Precipitation reactions can also be used to test for chlorides and sulfates in solution. These substances may be tested for in forensic work involving poisons or explosives residues. The test for carbonate compounds is a useful test for identifying rock types, for example in soil samples found on shoes.

21 The formula of the hydroxide ion is OH^-. Use this and the information in Table 4.4 to write the formula for a) copper hydroxide; b) iron(III) hydroxide.

Practical Work – Precipitation reactions

How to test for chloride ions

1 Dissolve the test sample in water in a test tube.
2 Add a small amount of dilute nitric acid followed by a few drops of silver nitrate solution.
3 If the sample contains chloride ions, then a white precipitate of silver chloride will be formed.

How to test for sulfate ions

1 Dissolve the test sample in water in a test tube.
2 Add a small amount of dilute hydrochloric acid, followed by a few drops of barium chloride solution.
3 If the sample contains sulfate ions, then a white precipitate of barium sulfate will be formed.

How to test for carbonate ions

All carbonates react with acids to form carbon dioxide gas. When an acid is added to a solid carbonate or a solution of a carbonate, then carbon dioxide gas causes the mixture to fizz or effervesce.

1 Add a small amount of the sample to a test tube.
2 Add dilute hydrochloric acid.
3 If the sample contains a carbonate, then the sample will effervesce (fizz).

Note: there are other compounds that will cause fizzing when an acid is added.

To confirm that the compound is a carbonate, we need to show that the gas formed is carbon dioxide. There is a simple test for carbon dioxide. Pass the gas through a solution of limewater (calcium hydroxide): a white (milky) precipitate will be formed. The white precipitate is calcium carbonate.

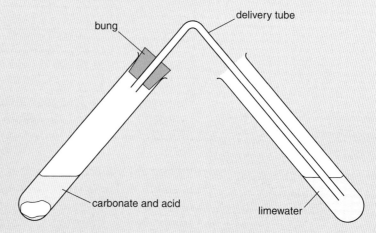

Figure 4.27 Apparatus for testing for carbon dioxide

Sample	Test	Observation
Chloride (Cl^-)	Add dilute nitric acid followed by silver nitrate solution	White precipitate formed
Sulfate (SO_4^{2-})	Add dilute hydrochloric acid followed by barium chloride solution	White precipitate formed
Carbonate (CO_3^{2-})	Add an acid such as dilute hydrochloric acid	Effervescence (fizzing)

Table 4.5 Summary of precipitation reactions

㉒ Give two different tests that could be used to show that a compound contains calcium ions.

㉓ An unknown compound gave a green flame in the flame test and also produced a white precipitate when silver nitrate solution was added to a solution of the compound. Use these two test results to give the name and formula of two ions present in the compound. Use your answer to give the name and formula of the compound present in the sample.

Testing for alcohol (ethanol)

Alcoholic drinks such as beer, lager, wine and spirits contain ethanol. When people drink ethanol, it affects the central nervous system and slows down their reaction time. This can affect the ability to drive safely and can lead to road traffic accidents. When a driver is involved in a road traffic accident, the driver will be asked to take a breathalyser test to see if he/she has been drinking alcohol.

There is a simple chemical test for ethanol. When ethanol reacts with acidified potassium dichromate, the potassium dichromate will change colour from orange to green. This reaction was used in the original breathalyser test.

Drivers who are suspected of drinking alcohol are asked to breathe into a breathalyser kit. The breathalyser test shows only whether or not there is alcohol in the driver's breath. It does show how much alcohol is present.

The latest breathalysers no longer use the potassium dichromate reaction: instead they measure the ethanol with a breathalyser that uses infra-red radiation to detect whether the driver has been drinking alcohol (see infra-red spectroscopy, page 120).

If a driver fails a breathalyser test, then he or she is arrested and taken to a police station. At the police station the driver will have to supply a sample of blood or urine. If the driver refuses to provide a sample, he or she can be charged with an offence.

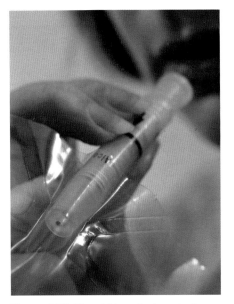

Figure 4.28 The old breathalyser test used a chemical reaction – if there was alcohol in the person's breath, the acidified potassium dichromate crystals turned green.

Figure 4.29 The new breathalyser test

The sample is then sent to the forensic laboratory for analysis. The forensic technicians will analyse the sample and will be able accurately to find the amount of alcohol in the sample.

The current alcohol limits are 35 micrograms of alcohol per 100 millilitres of breath or 80 milligrams of alcohol per 100 millilitres of blood. If the alcohol levels are higher than these limits, the driver will be prosecuted.

Practical Work – How to test for a reducing sugar such as glucose with Benedict's solution

Please see page 59 for more detail.

A positive result for glucose is that blue solution turns to brick-red precipitate.

Chromatography

Forensic scientists are often asked to analyse mixtures obtained from crime scenes or from suspects. They may be asked to identify the compounds present in the mixture, or to compare different samples to see if they are the same.

> **Chromatography**
> A group of techniques used to separate mixtures of substances based on differences in their solubilities

Chromatography is often used to separate the different components in mixture. This allows forensic scientists to identify the different components in a mixture – they can then compare different samples to see if there is a match.

One example where chromatography could be used is to investigate the ink used in a will or on a cheque. If the police suspect a document might have been illegally altered (forged), they can send the document to a forensic laboratory for analysis.

There are many different types of chromatography used in forensic laboratories. Two of the easiest chromatography techniques to carry out in school laboratories are paper chromatography and thin-layer chromatography. Both techniques separate substances by their movement when they are dissolved in a solvent (the mobile phase) through a medium (the stationary phase).

Figure 4.30 Forensic analysis can be used to check for forgeries.

Paper chromatography

Paper chromatography will separate a mixture containing two or more substances. The sample is placed on filter paper, and a solvent soaks through the paper carrying the components of the mixture with it. Different compounds dissolve better in different solvents, so the solvent used could be water, or an organic solvent such as ethanol (an alcohol).

Different substances are carried different distances along the paper. The component that is most soluble in the solvent travels more quickly and is carried furthest up the paper. The distance moved by an unknown substance can be compared with the distance moved by a known pure substance.

Investigating ink samples using paper chromatography

When investigating the ink used in a suspected forged document, the forensic technicians obtain samples of ink from different parts of the document by cutting out small sections of writing. The sections are then placed in separate containers of solvent to dissolve the ink from the paper. This results in different solutions of the ink used from different parts of the document. If necessary, the solvent can be evaporated to leave the ink as a more concentrated solution, or as a solid.

Practical Work – How to compare ink samples using paper chromatography

1 Using a pencil, draw a straight line (origin line) about 1 cm from the bottom of a rectangular piece of chromatography paper.
2 Using a pencil, mark with crosses on the origin line the places where the samples are going to be placed. Try to make sure that they are at least 1 cm apart.
3 Using a small dropper, place a small drop of a sample on one of the crosses. Allow the sample to dry, then add another drop of the sample in the same place. Repeat this procedure until you have a small, concentrated dot of sample on the cross. Then repeat the process until all the samples have been placed on the chromatography paper.
4 Suspend the chromatography paper in the beaker using a glass rod and paper clips, making sure the bottom of the chromatography paper is in the solvent, and the solvent level is below the origin line. Make sure the chromatography paper does not touch the sides of the beaker.
5 Place a cover over the beaker and leave the chromatogram to develop.
6 When the solvent front reaches about 1 cm from the top of the chromatography paper, carefully remove the paper from the beaker and allow it to dry. (The position of the solvent front should be marked on the chromatography paper if R_F values are being used – see page 119.)

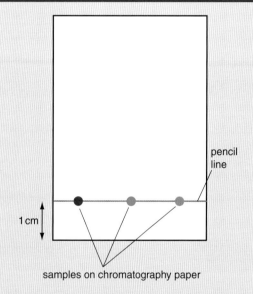

samples on chromatography paper

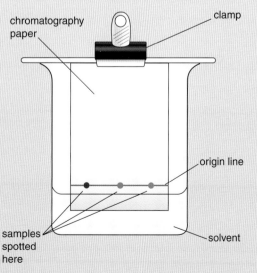

Figure 4.31 Apparatus for paper chromatography

24. Why is a pencil used to mark the origin line and positions of the samples?
25. Why is it important to have small, concentrated dots of the samples?
26. Why is it important to have a cover on the beaker?

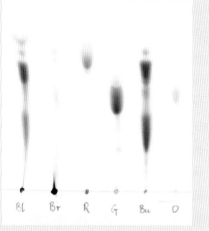

Figure 4.32 Paper chromatography can be used to compare ink samples.

Thin-layer chromatography

Instead of using paper, thin-layer chromatography (TLC) uses a plastic or glass slide that has a thin, even layer of silica gel or alumina spread on the surface of the slide. The layer is allowed to dry. The silica gel/alumina is the stationary phase (in paper chromatography, water molecules held on the surface of the paper are the stationary phase).

The samples are placed on a thin-layer chromatography plate, and a solvent is used to separate the components in the samples. One advantage of using thin-layer chromatography is that a wider range of solvents can be used compared with those used in paper chromatography.

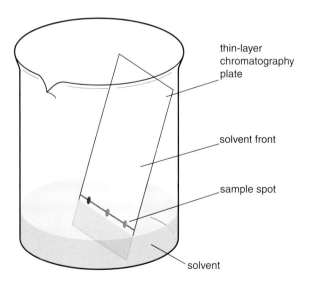

Figure 4.33 Apparatus for thin-layer chromatography

> **R_F (retention factor) value**
> A measurement from a chromatogram that can be used to identify the compounds present in a sample

The distance that each unknown substance moves on a chromatogram can be used to calculate an **R_F value**. The R_F value from a chromatogram is compared with the R_F values of known compounds. This could be from a reference book, or from a control test. For example, a test can show quickly that a sample definitely does not contain a particular illegal drug at a detectable concentration. Drugs are often mixed with other chemicals, such as sugars or starches, to disguise the drug. Thin-layer chromatography can be used to identify the sugars that have been added to a drug powder, as different sugars (fructose, sucrose or glucose) have different R_F values.

To determine the R_F value of a compound, two measurements are needed. These are:
- the distance travelled by the solvent (up the paper or across the slide);
- the distance travelled by the compound.

$$R_F = \frac{\text{distance moved by compound}}{\text{distance moved by solvent}}$$

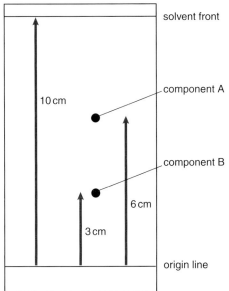

R_F component A $= \frac{6}{10} = 0.6$

R_F component B $= \frac{3}{10} = 0.3$

Figure 4.34 Calculating the R_F value from the spots on a chromatogram

Forensic laboratories will use other chromatography techniques, as well as paper chromatography and thin-layer chromatography. These techniques include high-performance liquid chromatography and gas chromatography.

Instrumental analysis

The chemical tests described above are useful in identifying the compounds present in a sample (qualitative tests) – but there are also a wide range of instrumental techniques that give accurate quantitative results.

Examples of the instrumental techniques used by forensic technicians include mass spectrometry machines, infra-red machines, atomic absorption spectrophotometers and gas chromatography machines.

Mass spectrometer

Mass spectrometers are used to identify elements and compounds by comparing the masses of individual component atoms in the sample with a list of the relative masses of the atoms of different elements and compounds. In the mass spectrometer, the sample is ionised to form positive ions, which are then deflected in a magnetic field. The amount of deflection will depend on the mass of the ion. This allows the ions to be identified.

The pattern in the spectrum of a sample can be compared with the thousands of patterns of known compounds held in a database. This allows technicians to identify the compounds present in a sample. This technique is often used to identify drugs.

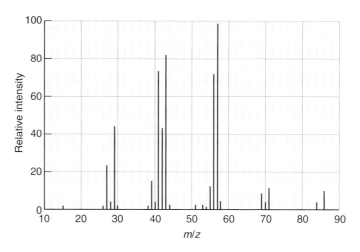

Figure 4.35 The shapes of the peaks in a mass spectrum of a substance identify the substance uniquely.

Infra-red spectroscopy

This is used in analysing covalent compounds. Covalent bonds will absorb infra-red radiation, and different bonds will absorb radiation of different frequencies. Infra-red radiation is passed through the sample, and the different frequencies that are absorbed are found. This allows technicians to identify different bonds present in a sample. Each different covalent molecule also produces a unique absorption pattern in a part of the spectrum called the 'fingerprint' region. This allows technicians to identify compounds by comparing their infra-red spectrum with a database containing the infra-red spectra of known compounds.

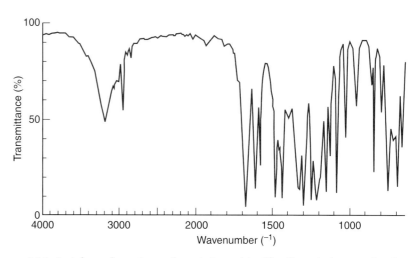

Figure 4.36 An infra-red spectrum of a substance identifies the substance uniquely.

Gas–liquid chromatography

This technique is based on the same principles as paper chromatography, but separates a mixture of gases. The sample is placed in the gas–liquid chromatography machine, where it is vaporised in a heated tube.

An inert (unreactive) gas is then passed through the tube. The inert gas carries the sample through the tube. The speed at which a compound passes through the tube depends on the relative mass of the compound. Compounds with smaller masses move more quickly. This allows the components in the sample to be separated. Each different component will have a different retention time (time for the component to pass through the tube). These retention times can be used to identify the different components.

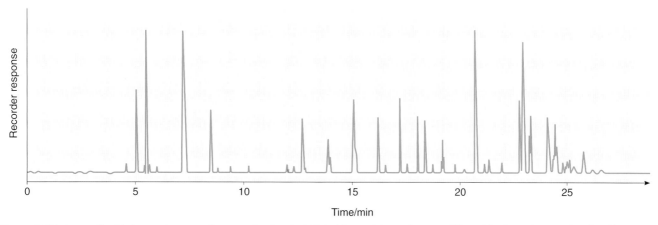

Figure 4.37 A gas–liquid chromatogram of a sample of petrol. Petrol is a mixture of many different hydrocarbon molecules. The trace of a fuel sample can be matched to a second sample of fuel owned by a suspected arsonist.

Atomic absorption spectrophotometry

This technique is very similar to the flame test. The sample being tested is heated to vaporise the sample. Light of different frequencies is then passed through the vapour. Different elements will absorb different frequencies of light in the same way that different metal ions give different colours of light in a flame test.

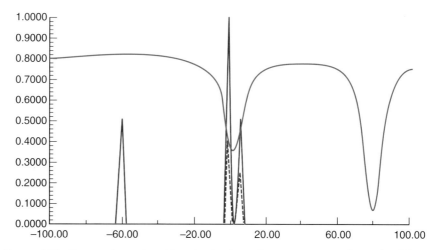

Figure 4.38 The graph produced by atomic absorption spectroscopy shows the different elements present.

Elements can be identified by the frequencies of light that are absorbed. The amount of the element present can also be measured in these machines. This technique is used to detect mercury and lead, which are common in poisoning cases.

Instrumental techniques have several advantages over simple chemical analysis. Instrumental techniques:
- are more reliable;
- are more accurate;
- use smaller amounts of substance;
- produce quantitative results;
- reduce human error.

2.3 Biological tests used by forensic scientists

For the Unit 2 written examination you need to know:
- the composition of blood (red blood cells, white blood cells, platelets, plasma);
- the four main blood groups: A, B, AB, O;
- that DNA is located in the nucleus of the cell;
- that DNA is unique to the individual (except identical twins);
- that children inherit their DNA from their parents;
- how charged particles move in an electric field and how this movement can be used to separate them (for example, in order to produce a DNA profile).

You also need to be able to use data, theories and explanations to:
- draw conclusions from the results of blood tests and DNA profiling.

Blood groups

Plasma
The liquid part of blood, mainly water – contains many important dissolved substances

Platelets
Cells in blood that form clots to seal wounds and control bleeding

Blood group
Every individual's blood is one of four main types: A, B, AB or O

The average person has about 5 litres of blood. Blood consists of a fluid called **plasma**, containing a suspension of solid particles. The solid particles in blood are red cells, white cells and **platelets**. Red blood cells contain haemoglobin, which transports oxygen around the circulatory system. White blood cells are much larger than red blood cells, and are part of the body's defence mechanism against disease.

Human blood is classified by **blood groups**. There are four main blood groups, given the letters A, B, AB and O. Table 4.6 gives the approximate percentage of the population having each of these blood groups.

Blood group	Proportion of the population
O	46%
A	42%
B	9%
AB	3%

Table 4.6 Blood groups in the population

Agglutination test
A blood test used to identify an unknown blood group

Antibody
A substance that reacts with specific 'foreign' substances on the surface of human cells

The blood group of a sample of blood can be identified using a simple test known as the **agglutination test**. Agglutination happens when the red blood cells stick together in large clumps. (When you receive a blood transfusion it is important that, if your blood group is O, for example, you receive blood from a donor of blood group O to prevent agglutination.)

To test for the blood group, known **antibodies** are added to different samples of the blood. The two antibodies used are anti-A and anti-B. If the blood is group A, then adding anti-A will cause agglutination of the sample; if the blood is group B, then adding anti-B will cause agglutination of the blood. Table 4.7 gives a summary of the results when adding the two antigens to the four different blood groups.

Antibodies	Group			
	A	**B**	**AB**	**O**
Add anti-A	Agglutination occurs	No reaction	Agglutination occurs	No reaction
Add anti-B	No reaction	Agglutination occurs	Agglutination occurs	No reaction

Table 4.7 Antibodies and their reactions

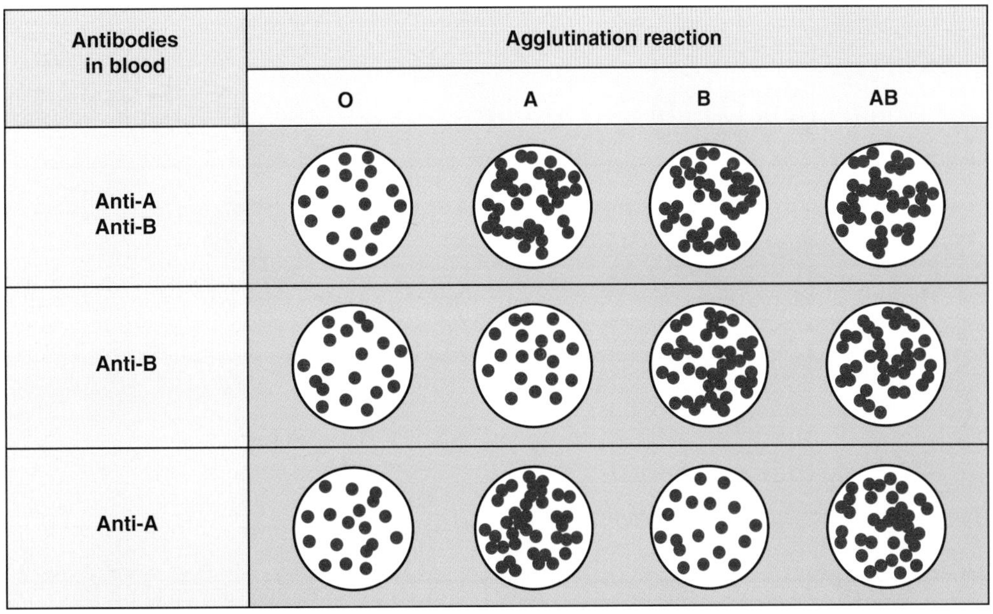

Figure 4.39 The agglutination test with two different antigens identifies one of four different blood groups.

27 Why does a positive match for group AB prove a better link to a suspect than a positive match for group O?

Finding the blood group of a sample of blood from a crime scene can help the forensic investigation. There are only four different blood groups, so there are millions of people with the same blood group. This means that identifying the blood group of a sample of blood found at a crime scene is more useful in helping to eliminate a suspect from a crime, than in linking a suspect to a crime.

DNA profiling

> **DNA profile**
> Also known as DNA fingerprinting – a technique to analyse and compare DNA samples

A **DNA profile** can be used to provide forensic evidence linking suspects to crimes, or to eliminate suspects. If a sample of blood from a crime scene has the same DNA profile as a suspect, then that is proof that the blood came from the suspect.

Except for identical twins, a person's DNA profile (or genetic fingerprint) is unique – different from the DNA profile of everyone else.

DNA is found in the nucleus of cells. Half your DNA comes from your father and half from your mother – it is determined at the point of fertilisation. The DNA will be the same in all body cells, including skin cells, blood, semen, hair roots and saliva. If the scenes-of-crime officers find any of these types of body cells at a crime scene, then the forensic technicians can obtain a DNA sample that they can use for DNA profiling. When the police want a DNA sample from a suspect, they usually take a swab of cells from the inside the mouth.

> **Electrophoresis**
> A technique that separates charged molecules by using an electric field and can be used to produce a DNA profile

For the test, DNA from the nuclei of the cells is cut up into fragments using enzymes. The DNA fragments are then separated by **electrophoresis**. This is a very similar technique to chromatography, but the samples are separated electrically.

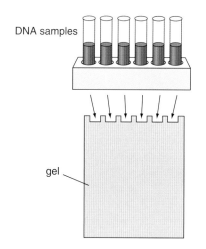

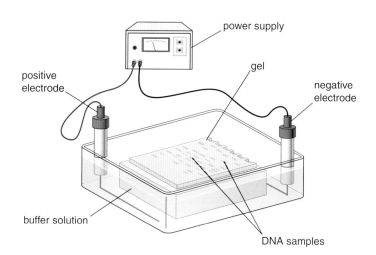

Figure 4.40 Apparatus for electrophoresis

Figure 4.41 DNA profiles

The DNA fragments are placed on a gel. An electric current is then passed through the gel. The DNA fragments are negatively charged and are attracted to the positive terminal. The fragments each have a different mass, and can have different charges. Fragments with smaller masses and larger negative charges will move through the gel more quickly. This allows the fragments to be separated.

The result of the DNA analysis is a pattern of light and dark bands (that looks like the barcodes used in shops). The pattern of light and dark bands on the DNA profile is unique to each person.

Electrophoresis is also used to separate proteins and amino acids, for example by trading standards officers checking whether a meat pie sold as beef might also contain other meats.

Other uses of DNA profiling

DNA is inherited from your parents – as a result, your DNA profile will have many details in common with your parents. DNA profiling is often used in paternity cases to prove or disprove who is the father of a child. DNA profiling can also be used to help in the identification of dead bodies when other means of identification are not possible.

Case Study – The Russian royal family

DNA was used to show that the skeletons found in a grave at Yekaterinburg in Russia were those of the Russian royal family. Several members of the Russian royal family had been executed after the Russian revolution in 1917.

The Russian royal family is closely related to the British royal family. DNA taken from the Duke of Edinburgh was compared with the DNA obtained from the bones found at Yekaterinburg.

The DNA profile of the Duke of Edinburgh showed a good match to the DNA profiles obtained from some of the skeletons at Yekaterinburg. This was sufficient to prove that some of the skeletons in the grave were the remains of the Russian royal family.

The use of DNA in forensic investigations is a relatively recent development. The first time DNA profiling was used in a court case in the UK was in 1980, when the DNA evidence led to the conviction of a murderer.

Some crimes that could not be solved a few years ago are being reinvestigated if there is any old evidence that can be used to obtain a DNA profile. Using the new DNA profiling techniques, several people have been convicted of crimes that they committed many years before.

2.4 Some physical tests used by forensic scientists

For the Unit 2 written examination you need to be able to:
- recognise the three distinctive types of fingerprint pattern (loop, arch, whorl);
- describe how light is refracted at a glass surface;
- describe the procedure to measure the refractive index of a glass block;
- describe how the refractive index of a glass fragment is determined;
- describe the distinctive features of fibres, bullets, seeds and soil that enable samples to be matched;

- describe the distinctive features of pollen grains and layers of paint;
- make measurements to enable a comparison of crime scene marks and impressions with real objects.

You also need to be able to use data, theories and explanations to:
- suggest which measurements or distinctive features of a mark or impression could be used to make a comparison;
- state whether there is a possible match between two different samples using distinctive marks or impressions.

How do forensic scientists test the different types of physical evidence, such as fingerprints, refractive index, bullets, casts of impressions, fibres and hairs, pollen and seeds?

Fingerprints

Fingerprints are often used to link a suspect to a crime scene. Although forensic scientists use the expression 'fingerprints', other parts of the body can leave identifiable prints: these include the palms of hands, the soles of feet and the prints of toes.

There are three reasons why fingerprints are particularly useful in forensic investigations:
- fingerprints are unique to the individual – no two people have the same fingerprints;
- fingerprints do not change over the years;
- the fingerprints of convicted criminals are held on the Criminal Records Bureau's database.

Fingerprints have been used for thousands of years. Over 4000 years ago, people in Babylon used fingerprints to sign their identity on clay tablets. About 2000 years ago, the Chinese produced fingerprint patterns in ink. In the nineteenth century, labourers in India would sign contracts with their fingerprints.

The first time fingerprints were considered in criminal activities was in the 1890s. In 1897, the Galton–Henry classification system for fingerprints was introduced. This resulted in many countries using fingerprint evidence in criminal investigations.

Fingerprints are made up of ridges on the upper skin on the hand. These ridges on the surface of the skin make lines. The lines are of different lengths and shapes, and produce a pattern. There are several different fingerprint patterns. The three most common are loops, arches and whorls.

loop

arch

whorl

Figure 4.42 Common fingerprint patterns

Typica
A unique line in a fingerprint pattern

Figure 4.43 Typica in a fingerprint

Fingerprints are compared by measuring **typica**. Every time a line in fingerprint pattern ends or splits it is called a typica. The positions of the typica can be measured and recorded. This is an example of a biometric measurement. If the typica of two fingerprints are the same, and are in the same places, then a match has been established between the two fingerprints.

It is not necessary to compare all the typica in a fingerprint pattern to show a match. Different countries require the comparison of different numbers of typica for a match to be established. Some countries require the comparison of 10 typica: if the 10 typica compared show no differences, that establishes a match between the fingerprints. Other countries compare 12, 14 or 16 typica when comparing fingerprints.

The measurement of the typica in fingerprints was once done by hand, and the comparison of fingerprints was very time-consuming. Nowadays fingerprints are scanned into computers, and the measurements and comparisons are made electronically. This makes the analysis faster, and also more accurate and reliable because it does not depend on human judgement. Once the fingerprints are stored in a database, comparison and matching take seconds to complete.

Obtaining fingerprints from a suspect

It is relatively easy to obtain a fingerprint record of a suspect using ink. The fingertips are rolled on an ink pad and then rolled onto a white card. This process is repeated for each finger.

Figure 4.44 Fingerprints being taken

Any fingerprints obtained at a crime scene are scanned into a computer. The fingerprints can then be matched with fingerprints held on the **Criminal Records Fingerprint Database.**

The police now have portable electronic fingerprinting kits. The fingers are placed onto a pad and the fingerprints are scanned electronically – the images can be immediately transferred to the Criminal Records Fingerprint Database for matching.

Refractive index of glass/plastic

Broken glass or plastic is often recovered from crime scenes and from road traffic accidents. Forensic technicians can examine the glass, and it is possible to match the samples to fragments found on the clothes of suspects. This is possible because of certain properties of glass.

When a ruler is placed in a bowl of water, the ruler appears to bend at the surface of the water. The ruler isn't really bent – it just appears to bend because of **refraction**. When light rays pass from water into air, they are refracted.

Figure 4.45 Refraction (bending) of light makes the part of the ruler in the water appear to be in a different place.

Each different transparent material will bend rays of light by a different amount.

This physical property, called the **refractive index**, is useful to forensic technicians when they are comparing different samples of glass obtained from crime scenes. Each different type of glass will have a different refractive index.

One method of finding the refractive index of glass is to follow the path of a ray of light as it passes through a glass block.

> **Refraction**
> Bending of a ray of light when it passes from air into glass or water
>
> **Refractive index**
> A measure of how much a ray of light is bent when it passes from air into glass or water

Practical Work – How to find the refractive index of a glass block

1 Place a glass block on a sheet of white paper and use a pencil to draw a line round the block.
2 Use a ray box to send a ray of light, at an angle, through the glass block.
3 With a pencil, draw at least two crosses on the path of the ray of light before it enters the glass block, and draw at least two crosses on the path of the ray of light as it leaves the glass block.
4 Remove the glass block, and use a pencil and ruler to show the path of the ray of light.
5 Draw a line at right angles to the block at the point where the ray of light enters the glass block, and a line at right angles to the block at the point where the ray of light leaves the glass block (these are called normals).

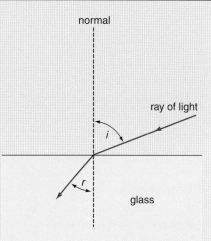

6 Use a protractor to measure the angle of incidence (*i*) and the angle of refraction (*r*).

The refractive index is then calculated using the sine of the angle of incidence and the sine of the angle of refraction.

Refractive index = sin *i* / sin *r*

In most cases, forensic technicians will be asked to examine small fragments of glass or plastic obtained from a crime scene. The glass block method can't be used to find the refractive index of small fragments of glass or plastic. For small fragments of glass, forensic technicians will use an oil bath to measure the refractive index.

The fragments of glass are placed in oil, and the oil is slowly heated and constantly stirred. As the oil is heated, the refractive index of the oil slowly changes. Very small fragments can be observed with a microscope while the oil is heated, and a video camera can record the image so it can be replayed. When the oil has the same refractive index as the glass, the glass 'disappears'. The technicians record the temperature of the oil when the glass fragments 'disappear'. They then use a data book to find the refractive index of the oil at that temperature. This will be the same as the refractive index of the glass fragments. If more than one piece of glass is tested, the measurement will be more reliable – the repeated measurement is a cross-check.

This method for measuring refractive index can also be used to measure the refractive index of pieces of clear plastic.

In some cases, samples of plastic are examined using a polarising microscope. Polarising microscopes can show examples where the refractive index of a material is different in different directions. This occurs in stressed glass and plastic. Using a polarising microscope provides a better match between samples of glass or plastic than just measuring the refractive index.

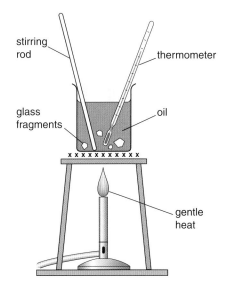

Figure 4.46 Oil-immersion temperature method to measure the refractive index of glass fragments

28 Why is the oil stirred constantly when measuring the refractive index of small fragments of glass?

Bullets

There are three ways to link a suspect to a crime in which a firearm, such as gun or a rifle, has been used:
* recovering bullets and cartridge cases and checking the calibre/manufacturer;

- analysis of any scratch marks on recovered bullets or cartridge cases;
- analysis of gunpowder residue.

The forensic science of **ballistics** is used to link bullets found at crime scenes to the guns that fired the bullets.

When a bullet is recovered from a crime scene, the forensic technicians will examine the bullet to determine its calibre (size), and then view it under a microscope to study any marks on the bullet.

Different guns use bullets of different sizes. The calibre of the bullet is used to narrow down the number of possible guns that could have fired it. The forensic scientists can also check any manufacturer's marks on the bullet.

Once the forensic technicians know the calibre and manufacturer of the bullet, they can use databases to find out what make of gun could have used similar bullets.

Rifling marks

When a bullet is fired from a gun or rifle, the barrel of the gun will create scratch marks on the outside of the bullet as it travels through the barrel. These scratch marks (**rifling marks**) on a bullet are unique to the gun that was used to fire the bullet.

The firing pin of the gun will also make an indentation on the bottom of the cartridge case. The shape of the indentation mark will be unique to the firing pin of that gun.

When the police recover a gun from a suspect, the forensic technicians can see if there is a match between the bullet from the crime scene and the gun.

The technicians will test-fire the gun to make a valid comparison between a bullet found at a crime scene and a bullet fired from the suspect gun. Normally they will fire the bullets into gelatin, water or other soft material, then recover the bullets. These materials are used so that no other marks are made on the bullet.

They can then use a **comparison microscope** to examine the two bullets at the same time. They can also use the comparison microscope to align the scratch marks on the two bullets to see if the markings are the same.

When a gun is fired, the explosion of gunpowder in the cartridge case results in some of the **gunshot residue** being forced out of the gun. Different types of bullet will have different cartridge cases, which contain a slightly different gunpowder explosive mixture. The combination of heavy metals present in the residue can be identified with an electron microscope or spectrometer.

Ballistics
The study of guns and bullets, and how they move when fired

Rifling marks
Marks scratched on a bullet as it passes through a gun barrel – different for different guns

Sample 1   Sample 2

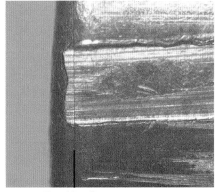

Breaking line

Figure 4.47 Two bullets identified as having been fired from the same firearm; the markings on each clearly line up.

Comparison microscope
Two microscopes linked together so that a direct comparison can be made

Gunshot residue
Microscopic particles of explosive ejected when the gun is fired – lead, barium and antimony compounds used in the explosive are detected when the particles are analysed

Gunshot residue can be blown several feet in the air. The residue will be on the skin and clothing of the person firing the gun. There will also be traces of the gunshot residue on anyone within a few feet of the gun when it is fired.

It is possible to obtain gunshot residue from the clothes of suspects. If there is gunshot residue on their clothes, this shows that the suspect has used a gun. Detailed chemical analysis of the composition of the residue can show a match between the gunshot residue and the cartridge cases of particular bullets. This provides stronger evidence to link a suspect to a gun crime.

When spent cartridge cases are recovered from a crime scene, the position in which they were found can be used to help solve a crime.

Casts of impressions

When the cast of a footprint or tyre print is removed, it is taken to the forensic laboratory, where it is examined. With casts of footprints, the technicians will look for patterns or distinguishing marks they could use to compare and possibly match with the footwear obtained from a suspect.

Some of the features a forensic technician would consider are:
- shape of the footprint;
- size of the footprint, including length and width;
- tread pattern;
- depth of tread pattern;
- make or manufacturer's logo;
- any distinguishing marks such as cuts, holes or other wear shown in the footprint.

Closer examination of footprint impressions in soft soil can lead to further information. The depth of the footprint (not the depth of the tread pattern) will give some information about the weight of the person producing the footprints. Heavier people will create deeper footprint impressions. By examining the depth of the impression at the front and back of a footprint, forensic scientists can work out whether the person who made the impressions was running or walking.

With impressions of tyre marks, technicians can take measurements that enable them to find the type and manufacture of tyre that made the impression. The forensic science laboratories will have all the different tyre sizes and patterns held in a database. This will allow them to identify the type of tyre very quickly. Any distinguishing marks, such as cuts or wear patterns, can then be used to match with the tyres on a suspect's vehicle.

When investigating impression marks made by tools, forensic scientists will use photographs of casts of the impression marks in trying to establish a match with a tool that could have made the marks.

Sometimes the tools used to break open doors or windows will chip small flakes of paint from the woodwork. Different flakes of paint can be compared by using a microscope to look at the pattern of layers in the flakes of paint.

Fibres

Fibres found at a crime scene can be used to link a suspect to the scene. The fibres are examined under a microscope to record features of the fibres. The fibres are placed on a glass microscope slide, either wetted or held in position by clear sticky tape. A cover slide is placed on top and the slides are placed under the lens of a microscope.

Several features of fibres can be used in matching samples. These include:
- whether the fibre is natural (e.g. cotton, wool, silk) or man-made (e.g. nylon, polyester, acrylate);
- colour and patterns of colour;
- texture (e.g. coarse or smooth);
- thickness;
- cross-section shape (e.g. triangular or round);
- amount of twist.

In many cases, the forensic service sends details of fibres to manufacturers. The manufacturers may be able to identify the fibres, and can inform forensic scientists of the companies that have bought the fibres from them. This can lead to information on the type of carpet, furnishings or clothes that contain the fibres.

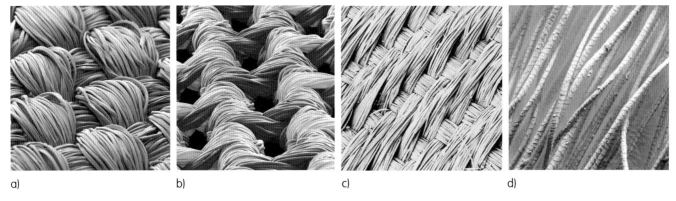

a) b) c) d)

Figure 4.48 Fibres compared under a microscope, a) cotton fibres woven to form a fabric, b) composite fabric knitted from nylon and polyester fibres, c) silk, and d) sheep wool fibres.

Seeds and pollen

Pollen grains are very small and can be examined properly only through electron microscopes, which give much greater magnification than light microscopes. Pollen grains can be identified by observing:
- size;
- colour;
- surface pattern.

Figure 4.49 Pollen grains under an electron microscope

Each different flower will produce its own pollen. The pollen grains from a plant are unique to that species of plant. This can be useful in linking possible suspects to crime scenes.

The clothes of a suspect can be examined for any samples of pollen. If there are pollen samples on the clothing, they can be examined and compared with pollen samples obtained at the crime scene.

However, a match of the pollen taken from a crime scene and pollen found on a suspect's clothing would not be enough evidence on its own to link a suspect to a crime scene. The pollen on the suspect's clothes could be from plants of the same species growing in a different area. Also, because pollen grains are so small and light, they are easily blown long distances from the plants. In some cases, pollen can be transferred from one place to another by insects or animals.

2.5 Unit 3 Investigation: Forensic investigations

In Unit 3 you have to complete at least one investigation for your portfolio. This investigation contributes 40% of the marks to the overall qualification. You will need to carry out an investigation, write a report and explain your findings. This section contains a possible investigation that could be used as the basis for your portfolio for Unit 3.

Where appropriate you should describe:
- how samples for the investigations are collected;
- how samples are prepared.

Having carried out your forensic investigations in the laboratory, you will prepare a report to present your evidence and conclusions (see Topic 4). The conclusions drawn from the facts should be explained and justified. Evidence that does not fit the conclusion should also be included.

Evidence could include actual objects from the crime scene, photographs or drawings, fingerprints or plaster casts, as well as experimental evidence such as chromatograms.

Remember this is worth 40% of your overall marks.

The techniques used in your investigations may include a number of the following techniques:
- testing the solubility of a substance in water or organic solvents;
- using universal indicator paper to measure the pH of a solution;
- using reactions and flame tests to detect the presence of metals;
- testing for ethanol using acidified potassium dichromate solution;
- using chromatographic techniques to separate coloured mixtures and colourless samples;
- examining surface details, such as scratch patterns or cross-sections of paint layers, using microscopy;
- comparing samples such as clothing, fibre, hair or small seeds using microscopy;
- determining the refractive index of small samples of glass and plastics;
- revealing and examining fingerprints on different surfaces;
- taking, examining and measuring plaster casts of footprints and tyre tracks.

Your investigation brief

A robbery has taken place at a remote country house. The house was entered by breaking a window at the back of the house.

The initial examination of a crime scene produces three pieces of evidence that could be used in solving the crime.

1 There was a good impression of a tyre-mark in some soft soil at the crime scene.
2 Some small pieces of broken glass were recovered from the scene.
3 A white powder was collected from the crime scene.

An abandoned car was found, with some glass splinters embedded in the upholstery of the front seats. A suspect was later arrested and glass fragments were found in some of his clothing. A different sample of white powder was recovered from the suspect's shoes.

As a forensic investigator, you are to examine each of these three pieces of evidence and produce a report of your findings that could be used as part of the evidence given in a trial.

You should carry out the following three tasks:

1 Make a plaster cast of the tyre-mark.
2 Measure the refractive index of the broken glass.
3 Analysis of the white powder from the crime scene shows that it is a mixture containing calcium carbonate and sodium chloride. Test the powder found on the shoes of the suspect to find out if it contains calcium carbonate and sodium chloride.

You will have to produce a report of your investigations in a form that could be used in a court of law.

Your report should include:
● details of the three tasks;
● clearly presented results from the three tasks;
● how the results of the investigation tasks could be used to link a suspect to the crime.

3 Interpreting the results of tests using databases

This topic contains material that you will need for the Unit 2 written examination and some techniques that you may have to describe in your portfolio for Unit 3.

In this topic you will learn about:
- the use of different databases by forensic services, and how the information is used by the forensic services.

Use of databases by forensic services

Some databases that are used in forensic investigations include: dental and medical records; vehicle records held on the Driver and Vehicle Licensing Agency (DVLA) database; insurance companies' records of valuable items; fingerprint and DNA databases; and police records of descriptions of missing persons.

If a match can be found in a database, this increases the probability of a positive identification. A mismatch can be equally important to eliminate a suspect from a police inquiry.

Dental records

Dental records have been used on many occasions to identify dead bodies. This is usually done only when there is no other method of identification available.

Dental records have also been used in the identification of skeletons and the bodies of victims of major accidents in which the bodies have been extensively burned.

Everybody has a dental record, and the records contain a lot of information that can allow a positive identification of a dead body.

This information will include details of dental work including extractions, fillings, crowns and bridgework. In some cases there will be records of X-rays of the teeth and mouth. If someone has had false teeth fitted, the dental records will include a record of the person's bite pattern.

Forensic scientists will attempt to match the teeth of the dead body to the records of teeth held on the dental databases.

Medical records

Medical records kept by doctors and hospitals can also be used in the identification of dead bodies. Anyone who has broken a bone or has had surgery in a hospital will have the details included in their medical record. This information could include written records of the surgery carried out or X-rays of the broken bones.

Police records

Witnesses can play an important role in the conviction of criminals. A witness to a crime may be able to help the police identify a suspect. The witness may be able to give the police a description of someone they saw at a crime scene. This information could include a description of their sex, ethnic type, height, weight and the clothing worn by the suspect.

The witness might be able to give details about the facial appearance of the suspect; this could include reference to their hair, facial hair, tattoos and scars. In many cases, the witness will be asked to help the police construct an image of the suspect. This image could be then used in the media (newspapers and TV) in the hope that someone will recognise the suspect and will be able to provide the police with further information about them.

The police have several methods of helping a witness produce an image of a possible suspect. They often use an artist to draw the face of a suspect, based on the description given by the witness. Once the artist has produced a sketch, it can be altered depending on any further comments from the witness.

The police also use computer programs – Identikit and Electronic Facial Identification Technique (E-FIT) – to produce an image based on witness information. These programs contain a large range of 'face parts' that can be used to build up a **composite image** of the person seen by a witness.

The police force has a national database that holds the records of convicted criminals. These records include the photographs and fingerprints of convicted criminals together with details of any previous convictions.

On some occasions, witnesses may be asked to look through the files of photographs of convicted criminals to see if they can recognise the face of someone they saw at a crime scene.

> **Composite image**
> Image of a face built up from a selection of 'face parts' to aid in identification

Figure 4.50 A composite photograph

DVLA database

The Driving and Vehicle Licensing Agency (DVLA) database carries information about all licensed vehicles and drivers.

The police can enter the registration number of any vehicle into the DVLA database and within seconds they have access to a large range of information, including the name and address of the owner of the vehicle.

If the police do not have the registration number, or only a part of the registration number, they can still use the DVLA database in their inquiries. If the police know the make and colour of the vehicle of a suspect, this information can be used.

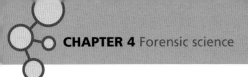

If the police input the make and colour of a car into the DVLA database, then the database will give them a list of every car that matches the description. The police can then use the list in their enquiries.

Suppose a witness told the police that a car they saw at the crime scene was a blue Ford Mondeo, then the DVLA database would list all the blue Ford Mondeos held on the database. If the witness could give any part of the registration number, then the list would include only Mondeos with that part in their registration numbers.

The police could then check the list for any owners that lived within a 20-mile radius of the crime scene. This would reduce the number of owners they would interview about the crime.

Closed-circuit television cameras (CCTV) play an increasingly important role in police work. In many crimes, the images of people and vehicles captured on CCTV have be used to identify suspects, and can also be used as evidence in courts of law.

Database	Information stored
Dental records	Extractions (missing teeth) Fillings, crowns, bridgework Braces False teeth X-ray records
Medical records	Written/computer records of operations Blood group X-ray records
DVLA	Name of owner of vehicle Licence number Make and model of vehicle Colour of vehicle Engine capacity Registration number, engine number, chassis number, vehicle identity number
Police records	Photographs Fingerprints Details of previous convictions

Table 4.8 Databases used by the forensic services

Crime scene case studies

These case studies are designed to give you the opportunity to show how forensic scientists use evidence found at crimes scenes to help the police solve crimes.

Case Study – Murder scene

The police were called to the scene of a violent crime. There was a dead body in a garden, and a cricket bat was found a few feet away from the body. The police sealed off the crime scene and sent for the scenes-of-crime officers and a forensic pathologist. The scenes-of-crime officers and the pathologist wore all-in-one white body suits, gloves and caps.

The scenes-of-crime officers took photographs of the dead body and the cricket bat.

The pathologist examined the dead body and used a thermometer to take the core temperature of the body.

The police could not find any identification in the clothing of the dead person.

When the dead body was taken to the forensic laboratory, X-rays of the teeth were taken.

29 Explain the importance of sealing off the crime scene and of the clothing worn by the scenes-of-crime officers and the forensic pathologist.
30 Give two reasons in each case why the scenes-of-crime officers took photographs of the dead body and the cricket bat.
31 Why was it important that the pathologist recorded the core body temperature of the dead body?
32 Explain how the X-ray of the teeth of the dead body could be used to identify the person.

Case Study – Hit and run

A man crossing a busy road was hit by a van that failed to stop. There were two witnesses to the accident, who were able to contact the police and were also able to give First Aid to the victim.

When the police arrived, the witnesses were able to give the police a description of the van involved in the accident.

The police used the information supplied by the witnesses and the DVLA database to identify a van that might have been involved in the accident.

The police visited the owner of this van and, when inspecting the van, they found some dried blood on the front bumper.

The owner of the van claimed that he had cut himself while changing one of the tyres, and that some of his blood must have spilt onto the front bumper.

33 Explain how the statement of the witnesses and the DVLA database would allow the police to identify a van that might have been involved in the incident, and how this information could lead to a suspect.

34 Explain how the forensic scientists could use the blood evidence to establish whether or not there is a link between the van and the accident.

Case Study – Burglary

The burglar alarm of an office was triggered by intruders. The alarm system was connected to the local police station. When the police arrived at the scene, they found that the office had been broken into.

The police sealed off the crime scene and sent for the scenes-of-crime officers.

The scenes-of-crime officers investigated the break-in and found several pieces of evidence:
- the glass in a window had been broken and some small fragments of glass were on the ground;
- some footprint impressions were found outside the window;
- some fibres were found stuck to wet paint on the window.

35 How would the forensic scientists:
    a) collect samples of the evidence from the crime scene?
    b) examine each piece of evidence?
    c) use the evidence to link a possible suspect to the crime?

4 Preparing a report and presenting it to a court of law

Having completed your investigation in the laboratory, as a forensic scientist you must prepare a report. The facts must be stated clearly, in a logical order. The conclusions drawn from the facts must be explained and justified in the report.

In this topic you will learn about:
- how to draw conclusions and interpret evidence;
- how you could prepare a forensic science investigation report for your portfolio.

For your Unit 3 investigation report you need to:
- produce a report of your investigations that:
  - describes the purpose of the investigations
  - includes a plan and risk assessment for the investigations
  - draws conclusions from, and evaluates, the investigations
  - explains how a forensic scientist might use the results of the investigations to indicate the probability of a suspect being linked to a crime.

Figure 4.51 Presenting evidence to a court of law

The last stage of the forensic process involves presenting evidence to a court of law.

The report that is presented to the court must be accurate. It must show that all the necessary steps in the forensic process were followed correctly.

The report should include:
- details of how and where the evidence was obtained – this may be in the form of photographs or written evidence;
- the results of any tests carried out will have to be given to the court – this could include written results of chemical tests, photographs of plaster casts or evidence from microscope work;
- scientific conclusions based on the results of tests – these need to be sound and reliable;
- sound forensic conclusions.

There is a difference between *scientific conclusions* and *forensic conclusions*. Some fingerprints are obtained from a crime scene, and a match is found with a set of fingerprints of a suspect held on a database.

The scientific conclusion is that the fingerprints are the same.

The forensic conclusion is that the suspect must have visited the crime scene at some time.

4.1 Interpretation of forensic evidence

For the Unit 2 written examination, you need to be able to use data, theories and explanations to:
- state whether observable features indicate a link between a suspect and the scene of a crime;

- interpret data and state whether there is a high probability that a suspect is linked to the scene of a crime;
- draw conclusions based on the facts and state whether, on the basis of the evidence, a suspect may have been present at a crime scene or may have committed a crime.

Forensic evidence plays a very important role in convicting criminals.

For Unit 3 (your forensic investigation) you will be expected to carry out a forensic investigation to compare and match samples in order to indicate the probability of a suspect being linked to a crime. You should remember that a match does not necessarily prove that a suspect has committed a crime.

But it must be remembered that forensic evidence on its own is not enough to convict a suspected criminal. Here are four examples that will help explain why.

- Fibres obtained from a crime scene were found to match the fibres from a suspect's jacket. There will be many jackets of the same make, and the fibres might have been used in making a large range of different jackets. The fibre evidence might be a possible link of the suspect to the crime scene – but the evidence is not strong enough to prove that the suspect was at the crime scene.
- Fingerprints found on a gun used to fire a bullet at a crime scene can only link a suspect to the gun. If the suspect's fingerprints are found on the gun, it only proves that the suspect had touched or held the gun – not when the suspect might have held the gun, or even if the suspect had fired the gun at the crime scene.
- If the cast of a footprint impression obtained at a crime scene matches with the shoes of a suspect, it does not prove that the suspect committed the crime. It only proves that he had been at the crime scene. It does not say when the suspect was at the crime scene – the footprints could have been made some time before or after the crime was committed.
- Broken glass recovered at the scene of a hit-and-run accident can be matched to the glass in a suspect's car. If the two samples match, it does not mean that the suspect's car was involved in the accident – there will many thousands of cars with the same type of glass in them.

Forensic evidence can be used to eliminate people from police enquiries. When a forensic scientist presents evidence in a court, the evidence given must:
- be impartial (based on scientific facts, not on opinions);
- be precise (easily understandable);
- stand up to cross-examination.

1 Forensic investigations follow a set sequence. Place the following steps in the correct order.
(3 marks)

Step in forensic investigation	Order
Interpreting test results	
Collecting samples	
Writing a report	
Recording the crime scene	
Presenting evidence in court	
Analysing the samples	

2 Select from the list of forensic techniques the one most likely to be used in each of the investigation techniques described. *(5 marks)*
  A Thin-layer chromatography
  B Flame test
  C Measurement of refractive index
  D Electron microscope
  E Comparison microscope

  a) Matching fragments of glass
  b) Examining samples of pollen
  c) Proving that a sample contains sodium ions
  d) Separating a mixture of ink
  e) Matching bullets

3 The police were called to the scene of an armed robbery. A witness to the robbery was able to give the police a description of one of the robbers involved.
  a) Suggest three facial features of the robber that the witness could include in the description. *(3 marks)*
  b) Describe a technique the police could use to help the witness construct an image of the robber's face. *(2 marks)*

4 Fingerprints are often used in solving crimes. A car was stolen – when it was recovered, the scenes-of-crime officers were able to obtain some fingerprint evidence from the inside of the car.
  a) Explain why fingerprints are a very reliable way of linking a suspect to a crime.
  (2 marks)
  b) Describe a procedure to reveal, lift and store fingerprints at a crime scene. *(2 marks)*

  c) Name three of the basic patterns in fingerprints. *(3 marks)*
  d) Describe how to take the fingerprints of a suspect. *(3 marks)*
  e) A match was found between the fingerprints found in the stolen car and the fingerprints of a suspect. Explain why this evidence alone is not enough to convict the suspect of the crime. *(2 marks)*

5 Simple chemical tests can be used in analysing samples obtained from crime scenes. For each of the tests given in the table, select from the list a chemical that will give a positive result in each case.

calcium ions   copper ions   sulfate ions
        chloride ions   ethanol
    carbonate ions   reducing sugar

Test	Chemical that gives a positive result
Gives a white precipitate when barium chloride is added	
Gives a green colour in a flame test	
Gives a green solution when warmed with acidified potassium dichromate solution	
Gives off a gas (effervesces) when dilute hydrochloric acid is added	
Gives a brick-red precipitate when heated with Benedict's solution	

(5 marks)

6 Some small pieces of glass were recovered from the scene of a hit-and-run accident.
  a) Describe how a scenes-of-crime officer would collect samples of fragments of glass from the scene of the accident so that they could be examined in a laboratory.
  (3 marks)
  b) Describe a method that could be used to find the refractive index of small fragments of glass. *(4 marks)*

7 A sample of a powder was found at a crime scene. A technician was asked to find the pH of the sample and to carry out a flame test on it.
a) Describe how the technician would determine the pH of the powder. *(2 marks)*
b) The pH value was 4.0 – what does this tell you about the sample? *(1 mark)*
c) Describe how to carry out a flame test. *(3 marks)*
d) Which metal ion would give a lilac flame test colour? *(1 mark)*

8 Laboratory tests on human blood can identify it as one of four different groups (A, B, AB and O). The results of blood tests can be used to link a suspect to a violent crime. The results of some blood tests are shown in the table.

Blood sample	Blood group
Taken from victim	O
Taken from suspect	A
Stain found in suspect's car	O

When questioned, the suspect said the blood in his car had come from a cut to his own arm.
a) What forensic conclusions can be drawn from the fact that:
   i) the stain is not the same blood group as the suspect? *(1 mark)*
   ii) the stain is the same blood group as the victim? *(1 mark)*
b) Explain why this evidence alone cannot prove that the suspect committed the violent crime. *(2 marks)*
c) Why is there a more certain match if the victim's blood and the blood stain found in the suspect's car were both blood group AB? *(1 mark)*
d) Explain how DNA profiling could be used to prove a definite match between the victim's blood and the blood found in the car. *(3 marks)*

9 A victim was shot in the leg during an armed robbery. The police found a gun at the house of the suspect.
a) Describe how the forensic technicians would try to find out if the bullet removed from the victim's leg had been fired from the suspects gun. *(4 marks)*
b) The police removed some clothing from the suspects home. Describe how the forensic technicians could use the clothing to link the suspect to the shooting. *(3 marks)*

10 Forensic technicians were asked to investigate documents that might have been forged. The technicians obtained two samples of ink from one of the documents.
a) Describe in detail how you would carry out a paper chromatography experiment on the two samples of ink. *(5 marks)*
b) State and explain three precautions you would take to make sure that the experiment is reliable. *(6 marks)*
c) The result of a chromatography experiment is shown below.

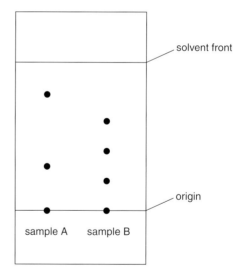

Give two reasons why the result of the chromatography experiment shows that the two samples are not the same. *(2 marks)*

Chapter 5
Sports science

How do you 'Bend it Like Beckham'? Do athletes have different muscles from the rest of us, or do they just have a better pair of trainers? What is in an isotonic sports drink, and do they make a difference? Why do Olympic cyclists wear pointed hats and full body suits, and what is 'fastskin'? The science of sport is fascinating and varied. Sports scientists aim to improve the performance of athletes competing in a wide range of different sporting competitions. Sports physiologists are interested in the health and fitness of parts of the body involved during exercise. Nutritionists and dieticians help to optimise performance by controlling energy and nutrient intake. Materials scientists develop new materials, and study their properties and the effects of the forces acting on them during exercise.

Success in sport depends on a wide range of factors, including:
- fitness of the body to perform in stressful situations;
- energy and nutrient intake before exercise;
- effectiveness of sports equipment and clothing used for training and competing.

On your marks, get set ... go! The start of a race, a high jump or football match all require our bodies to be perfectly tuned, and to work efficiently for maximum effect. Our heart, lungs and circulatory system work together to provide plenty of oxygen and glucose for respiration in the organs and muscles of the body. For athletes, this process needs to be highly efficient to provide the hard-working muscles with enough oxygen and glucose to work at maximum capacity.

Sports physiologists are interested in the health and fitness of athletes, and have a detailed understanding of the organs and organ systems in the body. This scientific knowledge enables them to monitor the human body during vigorous exercise, and to use this information to enable athletes to work at their maximum performance during competitions.

This chapter contains the theory you should learn to complete the sports science questions for the Unit 2 examination. For your Unit 3 portfolio, you may complete one investigation using the theory in this chapter. Two investigations are included in Chapter 5 that could contribute to your portfolio.

Chapter 5 is divided into three topics:

1 Exercise and the human body
2 Sports nutrition
3 Materials for sport

1 Exercise and the human body

In this topic you will learn about:
- the human cardiovascular system, and the breathing and heart-rate changes that occur during exercise;
- the breathing system, and how air gets into the lungs;
- aerobic and anaerobic respiration, and oxygen debt;
- how the body maintains a constant temperature and constant levels of water and glucose;
- how biceps and triceps muscles work in pairs.

1.1 The human cardiovascular system

For the Unit 2 written examination you need to be able to:
- describe the structure of the human cardiovascular system, including the function of the heart and lungs in providing glucose and oxygen to the muscles;
- describe the physiological changes that occur during exercise (breathing and heart rate);
- describe how the structure of the thorax (chest) enables ventilation of the lungs (breathing);
- measure pulse rate and recovery time;
- measure the vital capacity of the lungs.

You should also be able to use data, theories and explanations to:
- suggest suitable measurements to monitor physiological changes during exercise;
- explain the importance of taking accurate and reliable measurements;
- calculate pulse and breathing rate.

Cardiovascular system
The heart and blood vessels

Heart
A muscle that pumps blood around the body

Atria
The two upper chambers of the heart that receive blood from the veins (singular atrium)

Ventricle
The two lower chambers of the heart that pump blood out through the arteries

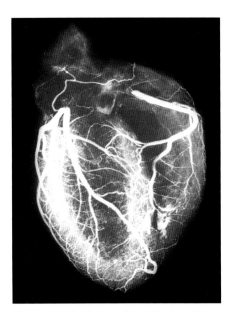

Figure 5.1 The human heart is about the same size as your hand when you clench it to make a fist.

Cardiovascular system

Muscles need energy to work. The energy comes from the food we eat. To release the energy from food, our muscles need oxygen. So how does the food we eat and the oxygen we breathe in get to the muscle cells in our arms and legs, or to our brain, to help us think and make decisions?

The heart, lungs, blood and blood vessels work together to provide muscles and organs with the oxygen and nutrients they need. Athletes train their heart and lungs to work harder and deliver oxygenated blood more efficiently, so they can get the maximum amount of energy for their muscles.

The heart

Your **heart** is the most important organ in the body. You can feel your heartbeat just to the left of your breastbone. The heart has four chambers: the top two chambers, where blood flows into the heart, are called **atria**. The bottom two chambers, where blood flows out of the heart, are called **ventricles**.

The heart is made of strong muscle because it has to push blood out of the heart and keep it flowing round the body. The left ventricle has to pump blood to the rest of the body, so its walls are the thickest, while the walls of the atria are relatively thin.

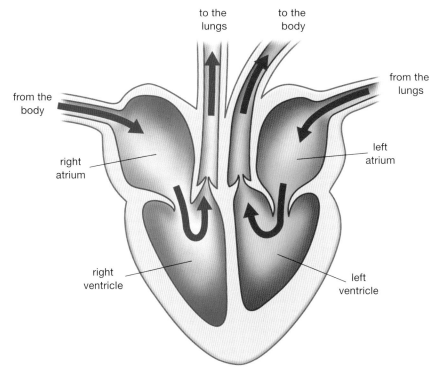

Figure 5.2 The chambers and direction of blood flow in the human heart

Blood vessels

The heart pumps blood around the body through the network of blood vessels called arteries, capillaries and veins.

Arteries are the blood vessels that carry blood away from the heart. The blood coming from the heart is at very high pressure to force it round the body. Arteries have very thick, muscular walls to help maintain this high pressure.

Veins return the blood back to the heart and carry blood under much lower pressure. The walls of veins are thinner, they have much less muscle than arteries, and they have valves to stop the blood flowing backwards.

Capillaries are the smallest blood vessels in the body, and link the arteries and veins together. They have walls that are only one cell thick, to allow substances such as nutrients, oxygen and carbon dioxide to diffuse in and out of them easily.

> **Artery**
> A blood vessel that carries blood away from the heart to the body
>
> **Vein**
> A blood vessel that carries blood from the capillaries towards the heart
>
> **Capillary**
> Tiny, thin-walled blood vessels that carry blood between arteries and veins

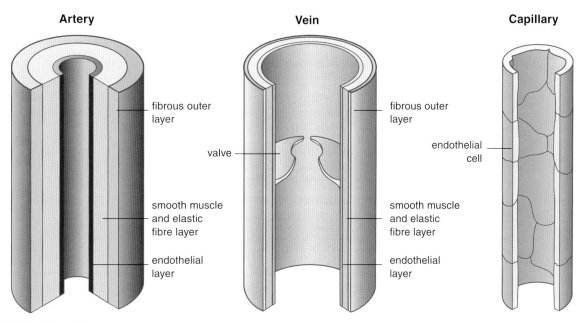

Figure 5.3 Blood vessels

Blood

Blood consists of a fluid called plasma, which contains red and white blood cells, and small particles called platelets. You have about 5 litres of blood flowing through the blood vessels in your body, transporting oxygen, nutrients (digested food) and other important chemicals to all the muscles and organs around your body, and taking away carbon dioxide.

Glucose is the primary source of energy for the organs and muscles in the body. Glucose and other nutrients are provided by digestion of the food we eat, and are absorbed into the blood from the small intestine.

The glucose is carried in the plasma part of the blood. The oxygen is carried by the red blood cells, and is added to the blood in the lungs.

Pathway of blood travelling through the heart

Humans have a double circulatory system. This is because as the blood travels around the body, it goes through the heart twice. The extra loop is a circulation to the lungs.

Blood coming from the body has less oxygen in it. This blood is transported in a vein to the right atrium in the heart. From here it travels down into the right ventricle. The right ventricle pumps the blood up out of the heart, through an artery, to the lungs. In the lungs, red blood cells pick up oxygen and drop off carbon dioxide. Oxygenated blood returning from the lungs to the heart in a vein enters through the left atrium and is pumped down into the left ventricle. The left ventricle pumps and pushes the oxygenated blood out, through arteries, to the rest of the body.

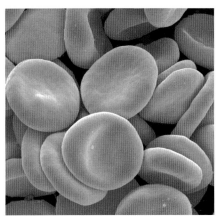

Figure 5.4 Red blood cells (magnification × 3150)

Pulse rate and fitness

> **Pulse rate**
> The number of times a heart beats per minute

The pulse is measured in the arteries. It is the pulse of blood being forced out of the left ventricle when the heart beats. The **resting pulse rate** can be measured in different places around the body. The normal resting pulse rate for most people is between 60 and 80 beats per minute. Athletes have a much lower resting pulse rate – top athletes can a have a pulse rate as low as 40 beats per minute. This is because they have trained their heart to work more efficiently. Their heart can pump out a bigger volume of blood in one contraction (beat). A larger volume of blood carries more oxygen and glucose to the muscles, so the athlete's heart doesn't need to beat as fast.

> **Aerobic exercise**
> Any exercise that makes your heart beat faster and work within 65 and 85% of its maximum heart rate
>
> **Recovery rate**
> How quickly the exercising pulse rate returns to the resting pulse rate

The **exercising pulse rate** is the pulse rate measured during vigorous exercise. This is the maximum heart rate. You can calculate your own maximum heart rate by subtracting your age from 220. If you are 15, then your maximum heart rate is $220 - 15 = 205$ beats per minute. Any **aerobic exercise** you do should be make your heartbeat between 65 and 85% of this number if you want to increase your cardiovascular fitness.

Athletes also have a lower exercising pulse rate. Because an athlete's heart is much fitter, it beats fewer times per minute, but still pumps a large volume of blood around the body. This means an athlete's blood can supply enough oxygen to the muscles during exercise. You could find out how this explains why athletes train at high altitude.

The **recovery rate** is a good indication of fitness. This is how quickly your exercising pulse rate returns to your resting pulse rate. It is usually measured at 1-minute intervals after exercise has stopped. The recovery rate of an athlete will be quick – this means their pulse rate returns to the resting pulse rate in a short period of time.

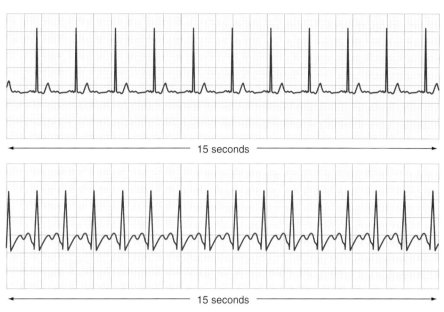

← 15 seconds →

← 15 seconds →

Figure 5.5 Electrocardiograms showing the heartbeat of an athlete (top) compared with a normal heartbeat (below) – the athlete has fewer beats per minute, a slower heart rate.

Practical Work – Measuring pulse rate as an indicator of fitness

Sports physiologists use the pulse rate to monitor how fast the heart is pumping. The pulse is felt at arteries around the body (the wrist, neck and groin are common places to measure the pulse). It is literally a pulse of blood being forced out of the heart by the left ventricle. Each pulse represents a beat of the heart. There are several different measurements physiologists can take.

Resting pulse rate: this is the pulse rate when the athlete is sitting down and doing very little – it is the rate at which the heart pumps when the body is doing the least activity. This can be used as an indicator of how fit an individual is.

Standing pulse rate: this is the pulse rate when the athlete stands up – the heart has to work faster to keep the blood flowing around the body.

Exercising pulse rate: this is the pulse rate while the athlete is training or competing and shows how fast the heart can pump during vigorous exercise – it can be used as an indicator of fitness.

Recovery rate: this is a measure of how quickly the pulse rate returns to the normal resting rate after vigorous exercise – this is also a measure of the fitness of an individual.

Taking a pulse rate

This procedure can be applied to resting, standing and exercise pulse rates.

Equipment
- Pulse-rate monitor (ideal) or a stop clock with seconds
- Pen and paper to record results

Procedure with a stop clock
1 Find the artery on your wrist by placing your fingers on the skin above the artery and apply a slight pressure.
2 You should feel a regular throb – this is your pulse (heartbeat).
3 Count the number of beats in 15 seconds.
4 Multiply this number by four to calculate the beats per minute.

You can use this method to calculate the resting and standing pulse rates. To calculate the recovery rate you can use the same method, but this time take the pulse rate every minute until it returns to normal (the standing or resting pulse rate). The recovery rate is the time it takes for the pulse to return to the resting rate.

Procedure with a pulse rate monitor
Each data logger will be slightly different, so it is best to follow the instructions provided. Most have a strap that fits around the chest and a wrist watch to take measurements. This is useful to measure pulse rate during exercise and to calculate the recovery rate.

❶ List the four chambers in the heart.

❷ Describe the pathway a red blood cell coming from the leg would take through the heart (remember to include the vessels and chambers).

❸ Give three differences between arteries and veins.

❹ Explain how the structure of a capillary is linked to its function (job).

❺ What part of the blood carries a) oxygen and b) glucose?

1.2 The lungs and respiratory system

Diaphragm
A sheet of muscle underneath the ribcage that contracts and relaxes to help the movement of air into and out of the lungs

Respiration
A chemical reaction in living cells that releases energy from glucose

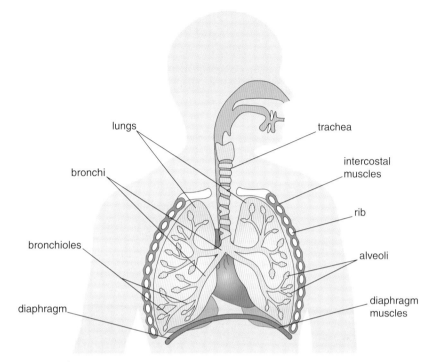

Figure 5.6 The respiratory system

Take a deep breath in … then breathe out … can you feel your rib cage getting bigger, moving upwards and outwards and then moving back in and down? This is breathing. Breathing is sometimes called ventilation of the lungs – it is the movement of air into and out of the lungs, similar to the ventilation of a building.

Breathing and respiration are not the same thing. Breathing is the actual movement of air into and out of the lungs by the movement of the ribcage, the rib muscles and the **diaphragm**.

Respiration is a chemical reaction that happens inside the body's cells. Oxygen, from the lungs, reacts in the cells with glucose digested from food to release energy. Carbon dioxide is produced by respiration. All living things must respire to survive, but not all living things breathe (think about plants). The lungs, heart and red blood cells work together to move the oxygen to other cells in the body for respiration.

The lungs

The two lungs in your chest are protected by the rib bones and muscles. Air is drawn in through the nose and into the trachea (windpipe). The trachea splits into two short tubes, called the bronchi, and these divide into smaller tubes, called bronchioles. At the end of each bronchiole is a bunch of tiny air sacs called alveoli. This is where oxygen diffuses into the blood, and where carbon dioxide produced during respiration passes into the lungs to be breathed out.

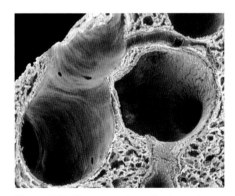

Figure 5.7 Air passes from the bronchus (blue) into the alveoli (yellow) where carbon dioxide and oxygen pass out of, and into, the blood during respiration.

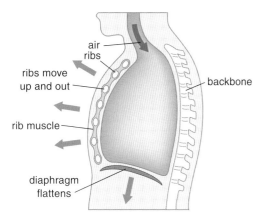

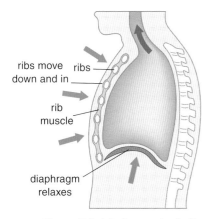

Figure 5.8 Inhaling and exhaling

Ventilation of the lungs

Ventilation of the lungs occurs when we breathe in and out. Ventilation involves the thorax (chest): the ribs, rib muscle and diaphragm. The process of ventilation is described below.

Breathing in:
- rib and diaphragm muscles contract;
- the ribcage is pushed up and out, the diaphragm is pulled flat;
- volume inside the chest increases;
- pressure inside the chest decreases;
- air flows into the lungs.

Breathing out:
- rib and diaphragm muscles relax;
- the ribcage drops down and in, the diaphragm resumes its relaxed shape;
- volume of chest decreases;
- pressure inside the chest increases;
- air is pushed out of the lungs.

We have seen that athletes can have a lower resting pulse rate because they have trained their heart to work more efficiently. They also have a lower breathing rate. This is because they breathe in more air in a normal breath than we would do. They take deep breaths that provide the lungs with plenty of oxygen.

Practical Work – Breathing rate

Just like the pulse rate, the breathing rate can be used as an indicator of how fit an individual is. The breathing rate is the number of breaths in a minute. One breath is breathing in and out. The fitter we are, the more efficient our lungs are, and the breathing rate decreases. This is because our diaphragm and rib muscles are good at contracting, so the lungs take in plenty of air each time we inhale.

Equipment
- Stop clock
- Pen and paper to record results

Procedure
1 Make sure the individual is relaxed and breathing normally.
2 Count the number of breaths taken in 15 seconds – breathing in and out counts as one breath.
3 Multiply by four to calculate the number of breaths per minute.
4 This method can be used to measure the breathing rate at rest and during exercise, and also how long it takes for the breathing rate to return to normal after exercise.

Tidal volume and vital lung capacity

Tidal volume and **vital lung capacity** are both measurements of how much air the lungs can hold.

Tidal volume is the volume of air inhaled and exhaled in a normal breath. This is normally about 400–500 cm^3, although this will be different for boys and girls, and for children and adults,

Vital lung capacity (VLC) is the maximum amount of air that can be inhaled and exhaled when you take a really deep breath. This is normally about 3 litres. Again, this will be different for different genders and ages.

You can measure the tidal volume and VLC of an individual using a spirometer. The spirometer measures the different volumes and then draws a graph. The sports physiologist can use this to see how well an athlete's lungs are working.

As an athlete gets fitter, their tidal volume and VLC increases. This means they are taking more air, and therefore more oxygen, into their lungs with each breath.

Physiological changes during exercise

As soon as we start to do any form of exercise, the body demands more energy. This means the cardiovascular system needs to provide oxygen and glucose to the working muscles much more quickly.

The changes that occur in the body during exercise are:
- the heart rate (pulse) increases – this means blood is pumped around the body much more quickly to move the oxygen and glucose to the muscles more quickly, and to remove the carbon dioxide and waste products from the respiring muscles;
- more blood is pumped with each beat – this means more blood is pumped around the body with each heartbeat so that more blood, carrying more oxygen and glucose, reaches the muscles more quickly;
- the breathing rate increases – this means we breathe in and out more quickly, moving the carbon dioxide out and the oxygen in much more quickly;
- the depth of breathing increases – this means more air is taken in during inhalation so that the maximum amount of oxygen can diffuse into the blood.

Athletes' bodies are in tip-top condition. Their heart and lungs work well together to get the most oxygen and glucose to the working muscles. They breathe in and out deeply, and pump out more blood per heartbeat to move more oxygen and more nutrients to where they are needed.

Tidal volume
The volume of air inhaled and exhaled in a normal breath

Vital lung capacity
The maximum volume of air the lungs can hold after a deep breath

The differences between an athlete and a non-athlete are shown in Table 5.1.

Function	Athlete	Non-athlete
Resting pulse rate	Lower	Higher
Exercising pulse rate	Lower	Higher
Recovery rate	Faster	Slower
Breathing rate	Slower	Faster
Tidal volume	Bigger	Smaller
Vital lung capacity	Bigger	Smaller

Table 5.1 Differences in fitness between an athlete and a non-athlete

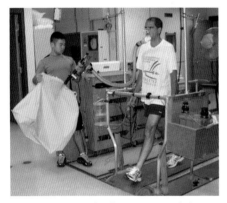

Figure 5.9 Douglas bags are used during training to measure the oxygen concentration in a sample of exhaled air.

6 Draw a flow chart to show the path an oxygen molecule would take once it had entered the nose.

7 Where in the lung does gas exchange occur?

8 What happens to the volume inside the chest when we a) inhale and b) exhale?

9 Write down the correct labels for (a)–(g) on the diagram below.

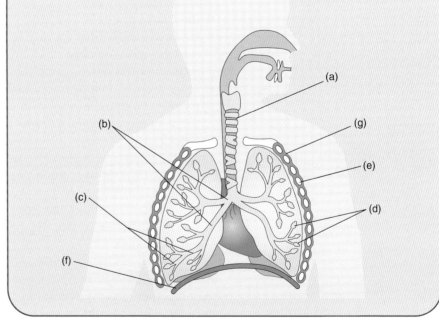

1.3 Aerobic and anaerobic respiration

For the Unit 2 written examination you need to be able to describe how:
- respiration may be aerobic or anaerobic depending on the availability of oxygen;
- oxygen debt may occur in the muscles.

Walking, running, eating and even thinking require energy – things we don't think about require energy. For athletes, the demand for energy is greatly increased. There are two types of respiration: **aerobic respiration**, which requires oxygen, and **anaerobic respiration**, which does not require oxygen.

> **Aerobic respiration**
> Respiration that occurs with oxygen present
>
> **Anaerobic respiration**
> Respiration that occurs without oxygen present

Aerobic respiration

Aerobic respiration requires oxygen. The oxygen reacts with glucose and releases the energy from it. It is a chemical reaction – the equation for the reaction is:

$$\text{oxygen} + \text{glucose} \rightarrow \text{carbon dioxide} + \text{water} + \text{energy}$$

$$6O_2 + C_6H_{12}O_6 \rightarrow 6CO_2 + 6H_2O + \text{energy}$$

This chemical reaction occurs in almost every cell in the body. It shows that we use the glucose from our food and the oxygen we breathe in to release energy. This energy is used to make our muscles contract, so we can move and run, and to help our bodies work properly. The waste products are carbon dioxide and water.

We produce a lot of energy from aerobic respiration – this is the type of respiration that occurs in our cells most of the time.

Figure 5.10 Sprinters respire anaerobically to get the energy to run – they don't actually breathe in throughout the race, but they take a lot of deep breaths when they have crossed the finish line.

Anaerobic respiration

For most activities, our bodies use energy from aerobic respiration. When we exercise, our heart rate increases and we breathe more quickly, delivering extra oxygen so that the cells can respire more quickly. However, if we exercise or sprint very hard, we can't get enough oxygen to release all the energy our cells need. The body can still release energy from glucose without using oxygen. This is called anaerobic respiration. When some trained athletes compete in short events, such as the 100 m sprint, they don't breathe at all – their bodies respire anaerobically.

The chemical reaction for anaerobic respiration is:

$$\text{glucose} \rightarrow \text{lactic acid} + \text{energy}$$

$$C_6H_{12}O_6 \rightarrow 2C_3H_6O_3 + \text{energy}$$

Figure 5.11 After hard exercise you may have an oxygen debt.

> **Lactic acid**
> A waste product that builds up when our muscles are short of oxygen and respire anaerobically

Lactic acid is produced as a waste product of anaerobic respiration. This is a mild poison, and makes the muscles ache. Once an athlete has completed a sprint, they will pant heavily to breathe oxygen into the

Oxygen debt
The oxygen needed to break down lactic acid that builds up in muscles due to anaerobic respiration during exercise

body again. Their liver breaks down the lactic acid so the pain goes away. The oxygen needed to react with and get rid of the lactic acid is called the **oxygen debt**.

Anaerobic respiration produces much less energy than aerobic respiration, but produces it more quickly. This is why the current Olympic champions can sprint 100 metres in under 10 seconds. For a marathon, you can't run at this speed because you need the full amount of energy released by aerobic respiration.

Although long-distance runners use aerobic respiration for most of a race, their bodies are working much harder than normal and so lactic acid is also produced. As they breathe in during the race, they provide enough oxygen to break down the lactic acid while they are still running – this can be described as a 'second wind'.

⑩ What are the products of aerobic respiration?

⑪ What is meant by the term 'oxygen debt'?

⑫ Which type of respiration would be used by
a) a marathon runner and
b) a 100 m sprinter?

Practical Work – Lactic acid in the arm muscles

Lactic acid is a mild poison to the body and is a by-product of anaerobic respiration. You can feel lactic acid building up in your muscles if you exercise them anaerobically.

Procedure
1 Put your arm high up in the air.
2 Clench your fist tightly.
3 Open and close your fist 30 times (or more if you can't feel it).
4 You can feel your hand and arm start to ache and tingle – this is the lactic acid building up in your muscles.
5 Shake your arm out and breathe in deeply – the ache should go away.

Case Study – A day in the life of a senior conditioning coach

Job title: Senior Conditioning Coach working at a Sports University

Job description: Design and deliver strength and conditioning programmes for a range of sports. This includes carrying out fitness testing for athletes for strength, power, speed, agility, body composition and endurance.

Qualifications: A degree or equivalent in Sports Science/Exercise Science with Strength and Conditioning qualifications. Additional vocational qualifications in Strength and Conditioning and SAQ

Award (speed, agility and quickness) are required, plus knowledge of Olympic weightlifting.

The work includes fitness testing for a national cricket team, testing individual athletes or whole teams (this can be university teams) and professional sports men and women. The fitness testing involves many different procedures that help give an overall picture of the fitness of the athlete and enable the coach to put together a detailed programme specific to the needs of the individual. The different methods used to assess fitness are:

- video analysis to look at technique;
- timing gates to test speed/quickness;
- jump mats for leg power and strength;
- body callipers to test body composition;
- **dynamometer** to test grip strength;
- use of **GPS tracking** on players to see where and how quickly they move during a game or race.

A sports physiologist carries out all physiological tests, such as pulse rate, breathing rate and measurements for vital capacity and tidal volume. Sometimes athletes are required to go into the physiology laboratory at the university to use specialist equipment such as Douglas bags (see Figure 5.9 on page 156).

The next job is to write sports programmes for the individuals and for teams. This may require research into the specific sport and supervision of a gym session to try out different exercises with the athletes. A fitness programme could be written for an individual athlete, a whole team or a member of a team, for example, a goalkeeper in a football team would have a different programme from a striker.

Finally, there will be a meeting with the coach, physiotherapists and psychologists to discuss the results of the tests and fitness programmes, and to decide the next steps.

Dynamometer
A device that measures muscular strength in a grip test

GPS tracking
Global positioning system device worn by athletes to monitor their response time and help as a part of their training programme

⑬ State three ways of testing an athlete's fitness.
⑭ Using your background knowledge, describe the techniques used to measure the physiological changes that happen during exercise, and why it is important to measure them.
⑮ Choose two different sports (e.g. a high-jumper and a scrum half in a rugby team). Think about how a fitness programme may be designed for these different athletes. What would you decide if you were the fitness coach?

1.4 How the body maintains a constant internal environment

For the Unit 2 written examination you need to be able to:
- describe how humans maintain a constant body temperature by sweating and changing the diameter of capillaries;
- explain why humans need to maintain the correct amount of water in the body (water loss through urine and sweat);
- describe how blood glucose levels are controlled by hormones (insulin and glucagon);
- measure the glucose content of blood and urine.

The human body is a remarkable piece of engineering. Sports physiologists and coaches continue to push athletes to their limits, yet we hear of new sporting records being recorded year-on-year. Is there any limit to how hard our bodies can work?

It is important that the conditions inside the body don't change very much. The cells in the body work best when the internal environment is kept constant – this is called **homeostasis**. Even when the external environment changes quite dramatically, or we push our bodies to work hard during vigorous exercise, the body is well equipped to adjust to these changes. We are going to consider three examples of this:
- changes in body temperature;
- changes in blood glucose levels;
- changes in water levels.

> **Homeostasis**
> The way in which our body maintains a constant internal environment, such as temperature, water and glucose levels

Changes in body temperature

In Topic 3 you will find out about the developments of new sports clothing and equipment that enable athletes to compete at their best – this includes helping athletes keep cool during matches or races. Here we are going to look at what actually happens inside the body when we get too hot or too cold.

A healthy body (internal) temperature is between 36 and 37 °C, and the temperature of the skin is about 5 °C lower. There are special cells in your body that detect when the skin temperature falls below or rises above the internal body temperature, and these send messages to your brain.

When we get too cold:
- the hairs on our body stand up on end and we get 'goose bumps' – this traps a layer of warm air close to your skin to help insulate your body;
- the blood capillaries near the surface of the skin become narrower, which means less blood flows near the surface of the skin so less heat energy will be transferred to the surroundings from your body – you may also notice that your skin goes pale, and your fingers and toes can go white if you are really cold.

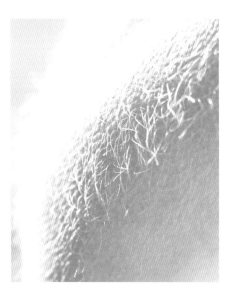

Figure 5.12 Goose bumps help warm you up by trapping a layer of air close to your skin

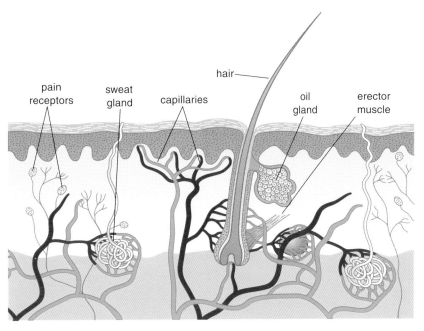

pain
receptors

sweat
gland

capillaries

hair

oil
gland

erector
muscle

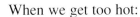

Figure 5.13 Human skin

Insulin was discovered in 1921, and production of the drug has saved millions of lives. Until recently, insulin was extracted from the pancreas of sheep, pigs and cattle. It is now made using genetically engineered bacteria.

When we get too hot:
- the hairs on our body lie flat;
- the blood capillaries near the surface of the skin get wider, which means more blood flows near the surface of the skin so more heat energy is transferred to the surroundings from your body – you may also notice that your skin goes red or pink because of the increased amount of blood flowing near the surface of your skin;
- the body releases sweat from pores in the skin – sweat evaporates from the surface of the skin and transfers heat energy from the skin to the surroundings – this evaporation cools the surface of the skin and the blood flowing beneath it.

Changes in blood glucose levels

As you have already found out, glucose is vital for energy, so it is important that we have the right amount in the blood. There is always some glucose in the blood, but the level can vary depending on what you have just eaten, or how much exercise you have done. In Topic 2 you will read about how athletes manage their dietary intake of different foods to maximise their performance. Here we look at what happens in the body if we have too much, or too little, glucose.

Too much glucose

If you eat a sugary snack or drink, apart from tasting pleasant, it will cause the level of glucose in the blood to rise quickly. Although glucose is an important chemical in the blood, too much changes the internal environment and your cells will not be able to work properly – it could even cause kidney problems. Special receptor cells detect this change and send messages to the brain:

Hormone
A chemical that is released from an organ or a gland and carried in the blood

Insulin
A hormone secreted by the pancreas when there is too much glucose in the blood

Glycogen
A carbohydrate used to store glucose for later use

Glucagon
A hormone secreted by the pancreas when there is too little glucose in the blood

- the brain sends messages to an organ called the pancreas, just below the stomach, and the pancreas releases a **hormone** called **insulin**;
- insulin is carried around the body in the blood and converts the glucose into a chemical called **glycogen**;
- glycogen can be stored in the liver and in the muscles until the body needs glucose again for energy.

Too little glucose

This time the brain sends messages to the pancreas to release a different hormone, **glucagon**. This has the opposite effect to insulin:

- glucagon is carried around the body in the blood to the liver and muscles and converts glycogen to glucose;
- the glucose is released into the blood ready to be used for respiration.

Changes in body water content

Water is essential for life, and keeping the balance right is vital if a sportsman or woman is going to perform at their best. It is also a waste product of respiration, so the body needs a way of keeping water levels right. In Topic 2 you will read about the different sports drinks that are now available for athletes. Here we look at what happens in the body if we have too much or too little water.

Too much water

The kidneys control the amount of water in the body. They are responsible for removing waste products such as urea and any excess water from the blood. If the level of water in the body is too high, the kidneys take out more water from the blood.

Waste products and excess water are removed from the body as urine – if there is plenty of water in the body, the urine will be very light in colour and have very little odour.

Too little water

This can occur when the body has become too hot and produced a lot of sweat. This time the kidneys take less water out of the blood.

A small amount of water is removed as urine – if there is very little water in the body, the urine will be dark in colour and have a distinctive smell!

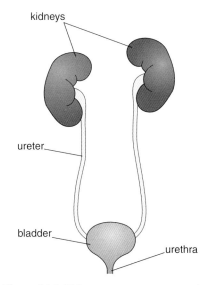

kidneys

ureter

bladder

urethra

Figure 5.14 Kidneys remove excess water and waste products from the body as urine.

⓰ Describe and explain the changes that occur when the body
a) gets too hot; b) has a low amount of glucose in the blood.

⓱ Explain why the amount of urine produced on a hot day can be much less than on a cold day.

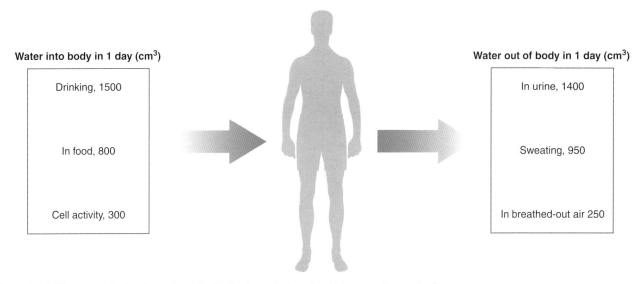

Water into body in 1 day (cm³)

Drinking, 1500

In food, 800

Cell activity, 300

Water out of body in 1 day (cm³)

In urine, 1400

Sweating, 950

In breathed-out air 250

Figure 5.15 The amount of water going into the body each day should balance the water loss.

1.5 Antagonistic action of muscles

For the Unit 2 written examination you need to be able to:
- describe the antagonistic action of muscles (triceps and biceps);
- measure the strength of a muscle using the grip test.

Muscle cells are often called muscle fibres. They are long muscles that group together in bundles. Under a microscope, the cells look stripy – this is called striated muscle. These cells are able to contract, which allows the muscles to pull (muscles cannot push). The contraction of muscles is controlled by signals from the brain that travel down nerve cells and makes us move our arms and legs where we want them to go.

When a body-builder wants to lift up a heavy mass during an exercise called a biceps curl, it is the biceps and triceps muscles that are working together. They work as an **antagonistic pair**. This means that when the

> **Antagonistic pair**
> When muscles work opposite to each other – biceps and triceps muscles are an antagonistic pair

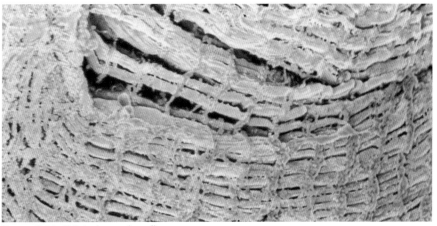

Figure 5.16 Striated muscle cells

biceps muscles have contracted, the triceps muscles are relaxed; and when the triceps muscles contract, the biceps muscles are relaxed.

A biceps curl

This is the same action that occurs when you just bend and straighten your arm. When the arm is bent, the biceps is contracting; to straighten the arm, the triceps contracts – you can feel these muscles move underneath your skin.

1 To lift the mass, the biceps contracts and the arm bends at the elbow joint. The triceps relaxes at the same time.
2 To straighten the arm again, the triceps contracts. At the same time the biceps relaxes.

Figure 5.17 A biceps curl

18 What does the term 'antagonistic pairs' mean?

19 Which muscles contract to bend your arm?

Practical Work – Looking at muscle cells under microscope

There are different kinds of muscle tissue in your body. Your heart is a muscle made up from cardiac muscle tissue; the wall of your gut also has muscle in it to help move food down. Being able to identify different types of tissue is important for many different scientists.

Equipment
- Light microscope
- Prepared slides of muscle tissue

Procedure
1 Set up the light microscope.
2 Focus muscle tissue under the microscope.
3 Look at different types of muscle cell, in particular the striated muscles that can contract.

Case Study – Body of evidence

Having the right body to suit a particular sport can make the difference between success and failure. Vivienne Parry looks at how athletes' build affect their performance

Adapted from *The Guardian* newspaper online, Thursday 5 August 2004

Top marathon runners tend to be lean and light, star swimmers are gangly things with huge feet and gold medal weightlifters are solid blocks of muscle with short arms and legs. So does your physique – and indeed the way your body works – fit you for a particular sport, or does your body develop a certain way because of your chosen sport?

'It's about 55:45, genes to environment,' says Mike Rennie, professor of clinical physiology at the University of Nottingham Medical School. 'There are identical twins from Germany, one of whom was an endurance athlete, the other a power sportsman. They look quite different, despite being identical twins.'

But having the right physique for the right sport is a good starting point. Seventeen years ago, the Australian Institute of Sport started a national Talent Search Programme, which scoured schools for 14–16-year-olds with the potential to be elite athletes. One of their first finds was Megan Still. In 1987, she had never picked up an oar in her life. But she had almost the perfect physique for a rower. After intensive training, she won gold in women's rowing in the 1996 Atlanta Olympics.

Swimming
The perfect swimmer is tall, with very long limbs, particularly arms. Top-class swimmers have big feet, which provide a huge propulsive advantage. They have big hands to act as paddles, narrow hips to reduce drag, and broad shoulders to maximise arm power. Sprint swimmers are more **mesomorphic**, with high-power energy systems.

Sprinting
The perfect 100 m sprinter is tall, with a strong mesomorphic body shape. Top sprinters have slim lower legs and relatively narrow hips, which gives a biomechanical advantage. They have a high percentage of fast twitch fibres (more than 80%). They use muscle fuel so fast that they are practically running on empty by the end of the race.

Marathon running
The perfect marathon runner has a light frame, slim legs, and is of small to medium height. They have high percentage of slow twitch fibres and very high maximal oxygen uptake. They can withstand dehydration, and training gives their muscles a high storage capacity for the premium muscle fuel, glycogen.

> **Mesomorphic**
> A type of body shape with well-developed muscles and strong bones

20 Describe the features that make a top-class swimmer and explain why their physique helps them compete at the top of the game.

21 What are the main differences between sprinters and marathon runners?

22 In your opinion, what are the main features that make a good marathon runner, and why are these features important?

2 Sports nutrition

In this topic you will learn about:
- daily energy requirements, and how they depend on an individual's mass and activity levels;
- body mass index as an indicator of ideal weight;
- why athletes increase their intake of complex carbohydrates before competing;
- why some athletes eat a diet high in protein;
- the composition of isotonic sports drinks;
- methods used to record dietary habits of individuals;
- indicators of fitness and health, and taking baseline measurements.

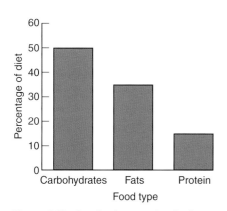

Figure 5.18 Graph of energy intake for normal UK diet

Cake, crisps, chocolate and fizzy drinks make up the diet of many teenagers – but is this what you would expect to see David Beckham, Jonny Wilkinson or Kelly Holmes eating before a big match or race? Food is our fuel, like petrol is for a car, and it is important that we put the right food in to get the best performance out. There is more about diet in Chapter 3. The right fuel for us is a combination of carbohydrates, protein and fats, along with smaller amounts of vitamins and minerals. The amount needed varies depending on the type of sport the athlete does – some athletes can eat up to twice as much as a normal person. Sports nutritionists work with teams and individuals to help them work out their **basic energy requirement (BER)** and their **extra energy requirement (EER)**, and then advise them on their dietary intake of these essential fuels.

2.1 Energy requirements

For the Unit 2 written examination you need to be able to:
- describe how the daily energy requirements for an individual depend on the mass of the individual, and that these requirements increase during exercise;

- calculate basic energy requirement (BER);
- explain why athletes increase their intake of complex carbohydrates before competing.

You should also be able to assess the applications and implications of science when comparing and contrasting:
- a normally balanced diet with that of a person competing in sport;
- a range of different diets – suggest their suitability for an athlete.

You found out in Topic 1 about how your body gets energy from food through respiration – but how much energy do you really need? Do athletes need more energy, or are their bodies just better? Athletes are not all the same size either.

Basic energy requirement (BER)

> **BER – basic energy requirement**
> The minimum amount of energy required for a person to do normal everyday activities

The BER is the amount of energy an individual needs to do normal things during the day – more energy is needed for training and vigorous exercise. For every kg of body weight, 5.4 kJ (1.3 kcal) is required every hour. To work out the basic energy requirements for a day (24 hours), you need to know the mass in kg of the individual.

Example

The BER for an athlete who weighs 75 kg

$= (5.4 \times 24) \times 75 = 9720$ kJ/day

Extra energy requirement (EER)

For each hour's training, you require an additional 35.6 kJ (8.5 kcal) for each kg of body weight.

The daily energy requirement for an individual = BER + EER

Figure 5.19 Athletes come in all shapes and sizes.

Example

For our athlete weighing 75 kg, who does 2 hours' training a day:

The BER is 9720 kJ/day

> **EER – extra energy requirement**
> The extra energy a person needs if they do exercise

The EER is $35.6 \times 2 = 71.2$ kJ/day

The **daily energy requirement** is $9720 + 71.2 = 9791.2$ kJ/day

> **Daily energy requirement**
> BER + EER

You can see that the more you weigh, the more energy you need to do everyday actions. If you increase the amount of exercise, you do you need to increase your energy intake.

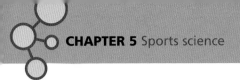

How much carbohydrate, protein and fat should an athlete eat?

Different types of food contain different amounts of energy. Fats contain the most energy, but it is difficult for the body to obtain it – so although fatty foods may taste good, they are not great for our body. The best energy source for the body is carbohydrate, because the brain and muscles can obtain the energy from it easily. The body needs protein to help it repair itself and grow, but we don't get energy from the protein we eat.

Energy source	kJ/g	kcal/g
Carbohydrate	16	3.75
Fat	37	9.0
Protein*	17	4.0
Alcohol	29	7.0
*The value for protein represents the available metabolisable energy, not the total chemical potential energy available from protein.		

Table 5.2 Energy equivalents of dietary macronutrients

2.2 Body mass index (BMI) as an indicator of ideal weight

For the Unit 2 written examination you need to:
- explain that body mass index is an indicator of ideal weight;
- be able to calculate BMI (weight/height^2).

> **BMI – body mass index**
> A measure of ideal weight

The **body mass index (BMI)** is used by nutritionists as an indicator of 'ideal weight'. It compares the weight and height of an individual, and can be used to determine if someone is underweight, overweight or obese by using a chart. There are other considerations that sports nutritionists need to consider, and they will use BMI along with other indicators to get a full picture of an athlete.

Calculating BMI

Nutritionists calculate BMI using the equation:

$$BMI = \frac{weight\ (kg)}{height^2\ (m^2)}$$

To calculate BMI you need to know the height in metres and the weight in kg of the individual.

Example

An athlete weighs 75 kg and measures 1.82 m

$$BMI = \frac{75}{(1.82 \times 1.82)}$$

$$= \frac{75}{3.31} = 22.65$$

This athlete is in the normal range.

Weight status	BMI
Underweight	<18.5
Normal	19–24.9
Overweight	25–29.9
Obese	30–34.9
Clinically obese	35–39.9
Extremely obese	40+

Table 5.3 This BMI chart can be used to show if someone is underweight, overweight or obese.

There are problems with using just BMI as an indicator. For example, a weightlifter or rugby player is likely to be short and very heavy. Muscle weighs more than fat, so their BMI could show 'obese' or even 'clinically obese', but they wouldn't have much fat tissue. So what else can nutritionists use as an indicator of a healthy weight?

Practical Work – Working out BMI, BER and EER

Equipment
- Scales (kg)
- Metre rulers – attached to the wall
- Calculator

Procedure
1 Weigh the individual (kg).
2 Measure the height of the individual (m).
3 Calculate the BMI (weight/height^2).
4 Calculate the BER for the individual using 5.4 J of energy for every kg of mass per hour.
5 Calculate the EER – you need to ask the individual to suggest how many hours of activity they do in a day. Add 35.6 kJ of energy per hour of activity.

㉓ Calculate the BER and the BMI for an athlete who is:
   a) 64 kg and 162 cm
   b) 83 kg and 171 cm
   c) 96 kg and 175 cm

2.3 High-carbohydrate and high-protein diets

For the Unit 2 written examination you need to explain why:
- athletes increase their intake of complex carbohydrates before competing;
- some athletes eat a diet high in protein.

You should also be able to assess the applications and implications of science when comparing and contrasting:
- a normally balanced diet with that for a person competing in sport;
- a range of different diets – suggest their suitability for an athlete.

High-carbohydrate diets

Carbohydrates are our primary source of energy – we obtain the energy from glucose during respiration. We can store carbohydrate in our muscles and liver as glycogen, which can be converted into glucose when it is needed. Some athletes, such as long-distance and marathon runners, increase their intake of carbohydrates before a competition – this is known as **carbohydrate loading**.

> **Carbohydrate loading**
> A diet where the muscles are loaded up with a lot of glycogen as a store of glucose for energy

About a week before a competition or race, an athlete consumes small quantities of carbohydrate and exercises to reduce the body's glycogen store. When this happens, the body 'thinks' there is a problem and reacts to the low carbohydrate levels by storing more glycogen than normal. About 3 days before the competition, the athlete consumes a diet made up mostly from carbohydrate, but also enough protein, vitamins, minerals and plenty of water, and reduces the amount of training to increase the levels of glycogen in the muscles. This makes the body restore its level of glycogen in the muscles, and encourages the muscles to store a little bit more glycogen too. When the athlete begins to compete, they have high levels of glycogen stored in their body. They can convert this glycogen to glucose to use for respiration to release energy.

There are side effects, though. These can include:
- muscle stiffness;
- diarrhoea;
- chest pain;
- depression;
- tiredness.

Figure 5.20 Weightlifters build more muscle mass by eating a high-protein diet

High-protein diets

Have you ever seen a weightlifter or a body-builder? Their bodies look very different from most people's – you can see every muscle in their body very clearly. Body-builders eat a lot of protein-rich foods, and train using heavy weights to build up muscle.

Protein is broken down into amino acids. This happens much more quickly during and after exercise, which means the amount of protein being made into muscle mass decreases because more protein is being broken down. The more intense the exercise, the greater the protein breakdown will be. Body-builders train to increase their muscle mass, so extra protein is needed to make up for protein breakdown, and also for new protein to be made and for muscle growth. Body-builders can't increase their muscle mass by just eating more

Figure 5.21 Creatine is a legal sports supplement that boosts muscle power. What supplements are illegal in sports?

protein; they have to train hard with weights to increase their strength or muscle size.

Sometimes athletes supplement their diet with micronutrients. These are useful nutrients that are needed in only small amounts, and work with the other nutrients they eat to make their bodies work better. Creatine is an example of a micronutrient that athletes can take.

> **Creatine**
> A protein-type substance found in muscles

Creatine is a protein-type substance found in muscles. It helps athletes obtain the maximum amount of energy very quickly. Some athletes, such as sprinters and weightlifters, take creatine supplements while they are training. The creatine is useful because their muscles don't get tired as quickly so they can train and compete harder, for longer.

2.4 Isotonic, hypertonic and hypotonic sports drinks

For the Unit 2 written examination you need to
- describe the composition of isotonic sports drinks (water, glucose and electrolytes).

Water intake

Water is essential for everybody. We are mostly made up of water – in fact, we are 70% water. Humans can live without food for more than 2 months, but cannot live for more than a week without water. Water is vital for athletes, especially when they are training. Different sports have different requirements when it comes to drinking.

> **Electrolyte**
> A substance, such as sodium or potassium, that dissolves in water to form ions

Dehydration

Sweating is one way in which the body maintains its core body temperature (see page 161) – this results in the loss of water and minerals such as chloride, sodium and calcium. Without replacing the water and the important minerals (also called **electrolytes**), the body can become dehydrated, which could result in death. Table 5.4 shows what can happen to the body when it loses water.

Figure 5.22 When exercising you need more water

Body weight lost as sweat (%)	Effect on the body
2	Reduced performance
4	Muscles can't work as well
5	Heat exhaustion
7	Hallucinations
10	Heart attack and heat stroke

Table 5.4 Effects of water loss

Athletes replace this lost water by drinking plenty of fluid before, during and after exercise.

Strenuous physical activity not only loses water in sweat, it also uses up the stores of carbohydrate in the body. Sports drinks have been designed to help restore the water levels in the body and to replace some of the carbohydrate used. There are three types of sports drink available, but you mainly need to know about isotonic drinks.

Isotonic drinks

Isotonic drinks quickly replace fluids lost by sweating, and supply a boost of carbohydrate. This type of drink is the choice for most athletes. Glucose is the body's preferred source of energy, and isotonic drinks contain a level of electrolytes and glucose similar to the fluids in our body cells – it is in balance with the body's fluids. This is why isotonic drinks are sometimes called iso-electric drinks. The electrolytes in isotonic drinks are mineral ions such as sodium, potassium and calcium – like the dissolved minerals inside blood and human cells. If you drank just plain water after exercise, it would make your blood more dilute, so your kidneys would produce more urine (see page 162) and your body would not rehydrate.

> **Isotonic**
> Having the same concentration of dissolved solutes as the fluid inside cells

Hypertonic drinks

These contain high levels of glucose, and can be used to supplement daily carbohydrate intake after exercise to top-up muscle glycogen stores. They are not so good at replacing the water part. Athletes often drink these with isotonic drinks to help replace water as well.

Hypotonic drinks

Hypotonic drinks contain very little glucose and a lot of water, so they quickly replace fluids lost through sweating. They are most suitable for athletes who need water without the boost of carbohydrate, such as jockeys and gymnasts.

24 Describe the main difference between an isotonic sports drink and a hypertonic sports drink.

25 Why do some athletes supplement their diet with creatine?

26 Explain the term 'carbohydrate loading'.

2.5 Methods of recording dietary habits

For the Unit 2 written examination you need to:
- describe methods used to record the dietary habits of individuals.

Think back to yesterday – can you remember everything you ate during the day? Maybe it's difficult to remember what you had for breakfast this morning! Nutritionists keep detailed records about the dietary intake of athletes. They can work out how much energy (kJ) an athlete has consumed, and find out the types and amount of food they have eaten, as well as when they like to eat their food. This tells nutritionists a lot about an individual, and helps them give advice and to design suitable nutrition programmes. There are many different methods used – two common ones are 24-hour dietary recall, and 3- or 7-day diet diaries.

24-hour dietary recall

This involves an interview between the nutritionist and the athlete. The nutritionist asks the athlete a series of questions to find out what the athlete ate the day before, approximately how much and the approximate time. It requires a skilful nutritionist to make sure they have an accurate picture of the athlete's dietary habits; it also relies on the athlete being honest.

3- or 7-day diet diaries

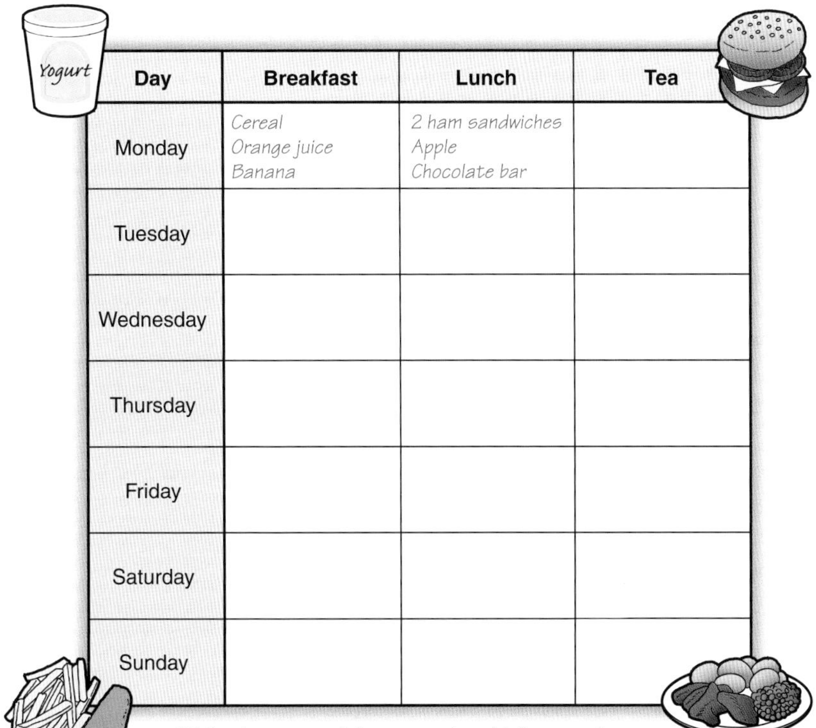

Day	Breakfast	Lunch	Tea
Monday	Cereal Orange juice Banana	2 ham sandwiches Apple Chocolate bar	
Tuesday			
Wednesday			
Thursday			
Friday			
Saturday			
Sunday			

Write down everything you eat or drink every day.
Don't forget to include those snacks in between meals!

Figure 5.23 A food diary

Diet diaries are exactly what they sound like: a detailed record of the type and amount of food eaten and when it was consumed. The diary is completed by the athlete, then used by the nutritionist to calculate energy intake and to analyse dietary habits. Diaries can be taken over a period of 3 or 7 days.

27 Here is an extract of a diet diary.

> **Monday 10 July 2006**
> Breakfast: 8.30 am
> Three slices of wholemeal bread, toasted and thinly spread with butter
> Two poached eggs
> Half a pint of milk
> Small glass of orange juice
> Medium-sized banana

Identify from the list a food that is a good source of protein, a complex carbohydrate and a fat.

28 Give three reasons why nutritionists use 24-hour dietary recall and diet diaries.

Case Study – Train like a Lion

The British and Irish Lions' nutritionist explains how to create your own sports diet

For their tour of New Zealand, the Lions took a full-time nutritionist with them on tour for the first time. This reflects a heightened realisation of the importance of consuming the right food and drink, for all athletes.

'Because each player is different, each one needs to have a specifically tailored diet,' explains Ron Maughan, professor of sports and exercise nutrition at Loughborough University and adviser to the Lions before they set off for New Zealand.

One of the nutritionist's duties will be to conduct hydration checks in order to advise players how much and what they should drink. 'There are a lot of factors. For example, not everybody sweats the same,' says Maughan. 'Some people secrete a lot of salt in their sweat and some secrete relatively little. It's vital that the former get a drink with salt if they're to recover quickly.

'Others may need a sugary drink. When you need to rehydrate in a hurry, water may not suffice because you end up peeing a lot of it out. Sports drinks are formulated to increase retention.'

Sports drinks such as 'Powerade', the sports drink of the Lions, also contain salts and sugar to replenish what is lost through sweat.

When it comes to food, though, the first piece of advice Maughan gives is simple: make sure you eat enough. 'One mistake many people make when they begin or extend their fitness regime is to start eating less because they think they'll lose weight that way. But if you've been running, say, 2 km a day and then you decide you're going to double that distance, and at the same time eat much less, then I'm afraid you're not going to last very long.'

The Lions have to eat well in the run-up to a tour. They avoid processed foods such as white rice and white pasta, and get protein from low-fat sources such as fish, chicken, beans and lentils. Their diet isn't totally spartan, however: 'Sugar can be a good source of short-term fuel,' explains Maughan, 'so judicious consumption can be effective.'

Adapted from *The Guardian* newspaper online, October 2004

㉙ Why do you think is it important that a national sports team like the New Zealand Lions takes a full-time nutritionist on tour?

③⓪ What factors do nutritionists need to consider when advising players how much, and what, they should drink?

③① What advice do the nutritionists give about eating food while on tour?

③② From your knowledge, what other advice could you give to the New Zealand rugby team?

③③ Imagine you are the Lions' nutritionist – what methods of dietary analysis could you use to investigate their eating habits while on tour?

2.4 Unit 3 Investigation: Measuring fitness before and after exercise

In Unit 3 you have to complete at least one investigation for your portfolio work. This investigation contributes 40% of the marks to the overall qualification. You will need to carry out an investigation, write a report and explain your findings. This section contains a possible investigation that could be used as the basis for your portfolio for Unit 3.

Your report should:
- describe the purpose of the investigation;
- describe how the investigation is connected with a particular sport;
- include a plan and a risk assessment for the investigation;
- make conclusions from, and evaluate, the investigation;
- explain how a sports scientist might use the results of the investigation.

Remember this is worth 40% of your overall marks.

Indicators of fitness

There are many different ways that sports physiologists can measure improvements in an athlete's fitness. Together with the measurements of pulse and breathing rate, lung capacity and BMI explained in Topics 1 and 2, you could use the following indicators to collect data for your Unit 3 investigation.

Indicators of stamina

Stamina means the ability to do something for a long period of time. Someone who can run all the way in the London Marathon has stamina. Someone who can do 1000 sit-ups has stamina. Stamina can be measured in numerous ways, but there are two really easy ones:
- the number of press-ups or sit-ups someone can do before they give up, or in a given time (e.g. 3 minutes);

- the length of time someone can sit with their back up against the wall and their knees bent at a 90° angle – this looks like the person is sitting on a chair that isn't there – and is much more painful than it looks!

You can see an improvement in stamina if someone can do more press-ups, or 'sit' against the wall for a longer time.

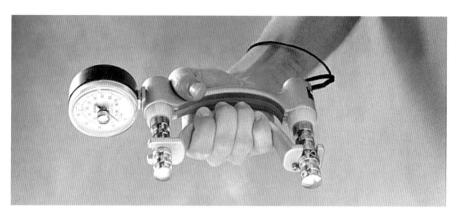

Figure 5.24 The dynamometer measures grip strength.

Indicators of strength

An indicator of strength is really about how strong your muscles are, so testing strength is easy to do. We have already mentioned one of them – the grip test using a dynamometer. The stronger the athlete, the harder they can grip. Another test would be the mass (kg) that an athlete can lift. This could be used to test the strength of muscles in the arms or legs.

Indicators of improved cardiovascular fitness

Anything that makes the heart beat faster helps to improve cardiovascular fitness. This could be running on the spot, doing shuttle runs, star jumps or cycling. The resting and exercising pulse rate, and the recovery rate, are all good indicators of fitness. How to measure them is covered in a practical activity on pages 151–152.

If an athlete has a fit heart and lungs, their resting pulse rate will be low – for a top athlete the pulse rate could be as low as 40 beats per minute. The exercising pulse rate will also be lower in a fit person, but the heart rate will still become much quicker during exercise. The recovery rate is the time it takes for the exercising pulse rate to return back to the resting pulse rate. As a person trains their heart and lungs, their recovery rate also decreases. This means their exercising pulse rate returns to normal much more quickly, as their body is working more efficiently.

Figure 5.25 The chest press and leg curl test the strength of arms and legs.

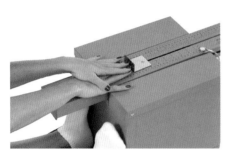

Figure 5.26 Sit-and-reach tester

Indicators of suppleness/flexibility

Flexibility for athletes is the range of movement the body can do. So if someone is very flexible, they can move their body into lots of different positions and shapes. Being able to touch your toes with your legs kept straight is an indicator of flexibility. The most common way athletes measure their flexibility is using the sit-and-reach flexibility tester. The further an athlete can reach, the more flexible they are. Athletes can improve their flexibility by doing stretching exercises.

Your investigation brief

Following a recent independent report on the poor fitness levels of teenagers in England, the Government has launched a new initiative to improve the fitness levels of young people. You are part of a large team of sports scientists investigating the short-term effects of simple exercises on the fitness levels of 15-year-olds.

You must design a fitness programme that will investigate the effects of short-term exercise on the fitness of teenagers. You need to make sure you can take measurements before, during and after the fitness programme to monitor their progress. Don't forget you will need to include a plan and risk assessment for the investigation.

The investigation will take about 4–5 weeks.

What you need to do

1   Decide which measurements you are going to take before the fitness programme – called baseline measurements. Some that you might include are listed below:

- pulse rate – resting/standing;
- breathing rate;
- vital capacity and tidal volume;
- grip strength;
- test of stamina;
- height;
- weight;
- calculate BMI, BER and EER.

2 Design a fitness programme. This needs to last about 25 minutes, and include warming up and cooling down. The programme should include a mixture of different exercises to target different muscles in the body. Some exercises you could include are listed below:
- stretches for leg and arm muscles;
- running around the playground;
- shuttle runs;
- star jumps;
- stepping up and down on a block or a bottom stair;
- cycling machine (if you have one);
- lifting masses – either in a gym, or you could use tins of baked beans.

The fitness programme should be repeated at least twice a week for about 3 weeks, to allow you to collect enough data.

3 Decide which measurements you are going to take during the activity, and which measurements you are going to take after the activity. Examples include:
- exercising pulse rate;
- recovery rate after running;
- the amount of mass they can lift;
- how far they can jump from a standing position;
- sit-and-reach test to test flexibility.

You may also want to repeat some of the measurements you took at the start.

4 What to do with your data – record your measurements in tables and graphs. In your report you should include clearly:
- what your results show about the measurements you had before, during and after doing exercise;
- how you could make your data more reliable or valid;
- how you could improve your procedure;
- how you could use this information if you were working with a sports team or individual athlete.

3 Materials for sport

Figure 5.27 Football boots today look a lot different – although they can sometimes still be made of leather, they also use a lot more synthetic materials.

In this topic you will learn about:
- the different materials used for sports clothing, and why sports clothing needs to be lightweight, durable and comfortable;
- why materials scientists need to consider the effect of friction when designing new clothing and equipment;
- the different materials used to make sports equipment, including the properties of these materials;
- the disadvantages and advantages of synthetic materials compared with natural materials.

Materials scientists are constantly researching, developing and testing new materials to see if they can help improve athletes' performance. They analyse the effect of forces such as friction and air resistance on the material used for clothing, and the ability of the material to absorb excess moisture, to help maintain the temperature of the body, or to encourage blood flow around the body. They design and test sports equipment made from materials that have the right combination of properties.

3.1 Structure and properties of different materials

For the Unit 2 written examination you need to be able to:
- give the characteristic properties of metals;
- give the characteristic properties of polymers;
- give the characteristic properties of ceramics;
- explain the properties of composites in terms of the properties of their components.

Scientists have discovered much about the way atoms bond together to form new compounds, and have a good understanding of why some bonds are harder to break than others, and why some allow materials to be flexible and malleable.

Many types of materials are used in sports equipment. The materials are used for different purposes – the use of each material depends on its properties. Commonly used materials include polymers, metals, ceramics and composites. The structure and properties of these materials make them good for their purpose.

Polymers

Polymers are useful because they are lightweight, flexible (bend easily), and good thermal insulators. They have a low **thermal conductivity**. Polymers are large molecules made up of many small molecules that are joined together by chemical reactions. The molecules form long chains that tangle up. The forces between the chains are weak, so the chains can move past each other. This makes polymers flexible.

> **Polymer**
> A long-chain molecule made of a lot of smaller molecules joined together
>
> **Thermal conductivity**
> The ability of a material to transfer heat by conduction

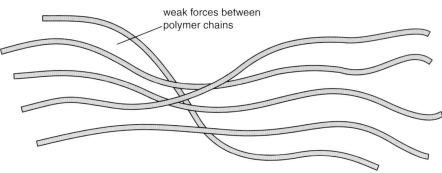

Figure 5.28 Long, entangled polymer chains

Some polymers are fibres, like polyester. Many synthetic polymers are plastics. PVC is a versatile plastic with a wide range of uses, because its properties can be modified by the use of plasticisers. These are small molecules that are added to the polymer to reduce the forces of attraction between the polymer chains, which makes the polymer even more flexible.

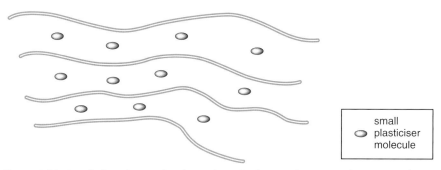

Figure 5.29 Small plasticiser molecules reduce the forces of attraction between polymer chains.

Thermosetting polymers form as a rigid, three-dimensional, cross-linked structure rather than separate flexible chains. There are no weak forces in the structure, only strong covalent bonds (see page 105). Thermosetting polymers are strong and rigid.

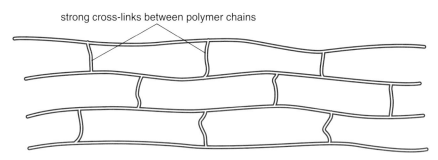

Figure 5.30 A cross-linked polymer – this plastic is strong and rigid.

Metals

Tensile strength
The force required to break a material when you stretch it

Metals are useful to most people because they conduct heat and electricity, but for the sporting world it is their hardness and high **tensile strength** that are important. They are not flexible – they don't bend easily.

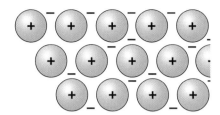

(+) positively charged metal ion

— negatively charged electron

Figure 5.31 Metallic structure – positive ions in a sea of negative electrons

Metals have giant structures. Metal atoms are packed together tightly. Each atom becomes a positive ion surrounded by freely moving electrons. The positive ions are held together by the forces of attraction by the positive ions and the electrons. This is called metallic bonding.

Metals can bond with other metals to form alloys – these are mixtures of different metals. Alloys have the properties of both types of metal.

Ceramics

Pottery is the best known example of a ceramic. Ceramics have been used for many years as building materials – tiles on spacecraft are an example of new ceramic technology. Ceramics are inorganic materials that are hard, have high melting points and low thermal conductivity, and are strong but brittle. An example of a ceramic is silica. This is a pure form of silicon dioxide and has a very high melting point, which can be explained by its structure. Ceramics such as silica are often mixed with other materials to produce composites.

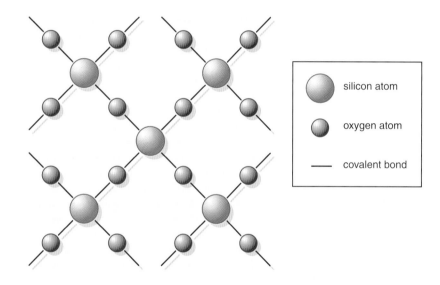

silicon atom

oxygen atom

— covalent bond

Figure 5.32 There are strong covalent bonds between silicon and oxygen atoms in the ceramic material silica

Figure 5.33 These days much sports equipment is made from composite materials

Composites

Composites are possibly the most useful materials in the sporting industry. Composites are combinations of two or more different types of material. They have the properties of both materials. An example of a composite is fibreglass. Glass is strong but brittle; plastic is weak but flexible. Bonding fibres of glass to plastic resin produces a new composite material that is strong like glass, but flexible like plastic. Fibreglass is stronger than wood, but much lighter – it is ideal for making small boats.

Figure 5.34 LYCRA® body suits help make athletes more aerodynamic.

3.2 Materials used for sports clothing

For the Unit 2 written exam you need to:
- explain why sports clothing (including footwear) needs to be lightweight, durable and comfortable;
- give examples of different types of materials (natural – cotton, leather; synthetic – polyester, LYCRA®) used for sports clothing;
- describe the disadvantages and advantages of synthetic materials compared with natural materials;
- describe how different properties of materials are desirable for different clothing:
  - low density for increasing speed
  - smooth for aerodynamic shapes
  - high tensile strength for materials providing support
  - thermal insulation to help maintain body temperature
  - large surface area for cooling
  - flexibility for comfortable clothing
  - shock-absorbent materials for footwear.

You should also be able to use data, theories and explanations to:
- select appropriate materials for sports clothing, equipment and footwear and explain why the different properties are important.

Natural materials occur naturally in the environment. Sometimes they are found in the ground; sometimes they come from living things. Synthetic materials have been made from other products or chemicals. Table 5.5 shows examples of natural and synthetic materials, and where they come from.

Type of material	Material	Source
Natural	Wood	Trees
	Silk	Cocoons of moths
	Cotton	Cotton plant
	Leather	Cattle
Synthetic	Nylon	Crude oil
	Polyester	Crude oil
	Fibreglass	Composite of plastic and glass
	KEVLAR®	Man-made organic fibres

Table 5.5 Sources of natural and synthetic materials

Different fabrics for different occasions

'Faster, higher, stronger' is the motto of the Olympic Games, and at the very highest level this motto applies to all sports and athletes. Physiology, nutritional guidance and training can get an athlete so far – the last stage is the development of the right clothing and equipment in order to achieve the best.

The majority of sports clothing used to be made from cotton, but now the science of materials has become big business, and scientists have made new materials suitable for all sports, whatever the weather.

LYCRA® is a stretchy synthetic fabric and a great invention for the sporting world. Its main purpose was to keep athletes' shorts up – but it also makes garments more aerodynamic as they fit close to the body. Today, entire outfits are made from LYCRA®. Its elastic properties have also been used to treat injuries with compression bandages that stop swelling.

Phase change
Material that can change the state it is in – for example, a gel that can turn into a liquid

Phase change materials are a revolutionary design developed particularly for sportswear. These materials contain a chemical that changes from being a liquid to a gel at about 37 °C – body temperature. This changes the insulation properties of the fabric and keeps the body at a constant temperature, regardless of the temperature of the air. These fabrics have been used for hats, gloves and boots.

The fibres in the fabrics are really important. The new fabrics have special fibres woven together to help absorb the water produced by sweating. The new sports clothing draws moisture away from the skin so that it remains dry. A good example is football shirts made out of 'sports wool'. This is made from two fabrics: wool and polyester. The natural material is close to the skin to absorb moisture; the polyester is on the outside, and can be dyed with colourful designs and logos.

Figure 5.35 Phase change clothes contain a chemical that can change from a liquid to a gel.

'Sports wool' can be used for sports socks too. Materials scientists have spent a lot of time and effort designing and redesigning the sports sock! Now socks are good at absorbing sweat away from the body, and have anti-odour and anti-microbial properties that help protect athletes against the fungus that causes athlete's foot. The latest designs are also 'anti-friction', with two layers – the outer layer grips the shoe and the inner layer grips the foot, which means the socks don't rub the feet and cause blisters.

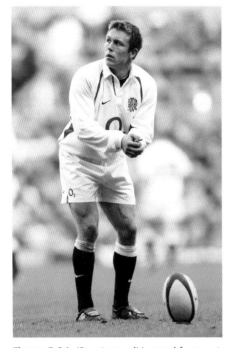

Figure 5.36 'Sports wool' is used for most football and rugby shirts.

Practical Work – Cooling properties of materials

Different materials keep heat in, or transfer heat to their surroundings. Materials scientists carry out simple procedures to test the amount of heat transferred away from the material to the surroundings – keeping the athlete cool. Sometimes scientists may want the material to keep the heat in, for example for winter sports clothes; other times they may want the heat to be transferred away, such as for running clothes.

Equipment
● Five different materials (preferably both synthetic and natural materials)

- Glass beaker
- Thermometer or temperature probes
- Clamp and clamp stand (wooden burette clamps would be ideal)
- Fan (optional)
- Kettle for warm water

Procedure
1 Moisten the material in warm water.
2 Wrap a different material around the bulb thermometer or the end of the temperature probe.
3 Clamp the thermometer or temperature probe into the clamp stand (take care if working with glass).
4 Record the starting temperature.
5 If you have a fan, turn it on.
6 Record the temperature every minute for 10 min.
7 Record your results in a table.

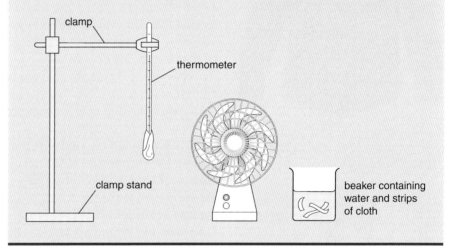
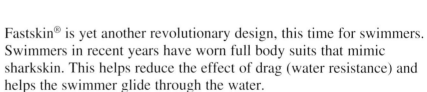

Figure 5.37 Fastskin® fabrics reduce drag when a swimmer moves through water.

Fastskin® is yet another revolutionary design, this time for swimmers. Swimmers in recent years have worn full body suits that mimic sharkskin. This helps reduce the effect of drag (water resistance) and helps the swimmer glide through the water.

Footwear

Sports footwear is a science by itself. The modern football boot is made up from five different types of material:
- kangaroo leather – to add that extra spring in the step (this is not a joke – in fact there have been a series of complaints from animal rights groups);
- KEVLAR® – for strength;
- leather/canvas composite – thin, stable and low-density;
- foam blown polyurethane – enhanced cushioning effect;
- thermoplastic polyurethane – for strength.

Figure 5.38 Many different materials make up the football boot we recognise today.

Different shoes have been developed for different sports, for example, for high-jumpers there is a thicker sole, and the shoe is light and flexible to help the athlete gain speed quickly. Sprinters' shoes are also lightweight and flexible, and have spikes at the front to be able to cope with different surfaces. Long-distance running shoes need to be durable and flexible, and able to allow the feet to breathe, to control the temperature and sweating of the feet. There is research into a new design of shoe that reduces the vibrations, and therefore damage on the muscles, when running. The shoes contain a special gel that 'tunes' itself to the running style of the athlete and can boost performance by up to 4%.

3.3 Materials used for sports equipment

For the Unit 2 written exam you need to:
- give examples of materials (wood, metal, polymers, ceramics, composites) used to make sports equipment (clubs, racquets, bicycle frames, protective equipment);
- describe the disadvantages and advantages of synthetic materials compared with natural materials;
- describe how different properties of materials are desirable for different equipment:
  - low density for increasing speed
  - smooth for aerodynamic shapes
  - high tensile strength for materials, providing support
  - thermal insulation to help maintain body temperature
  - large surface area for cooling
  - flexibility for comfortable equipment.

You should also be able to use data, theories and explanations to:
- select appropriate materials for sports clothing, equipment and footwear, and explain why the different properties are important.

Each sport has different needs and requirements from the materials they use. Sometimes natural materials are best; sometimes synthetic materials are more suitable – but whichever it is, that is possibly the last thing on an Olympic speed skater's mind as they hurtle towards the finish line on their 'poly-aromatic amide' skis!

Tennis rackets used to be wooden, and golf irons were literally made of iron. Materials for sports equipment are developing as quickly as materials for sports clothing. Advanced materials allow athletes to perform at the top of their game. The improvements in sports equipment have helped break more world records. In 1912 the 100 m sprint was run in 10.6 s, now the record is under 9 s. Runners in 1912 didn't have spiked shoes, Fastskin®, starting blocks or advice on nutrition and training.

Figure 5.39 Tennis rackets used to be wooden; today most are made from graphite or a composite material.

KEVLAR®

KEVLAR® has become one of the most important synthetic materials in the twenty-first century. It is a polymer that is five times stronger than steel, but is flexible, comfortable and lightweight. Among other things, KEVLAR® is used to make skis, helmets, rackets, sailboat sails, and land sails. This is because it is a super-strong material, but very lightweight.

Figure 5.40 KEVLAR®

Graphite

This is a carbon-based material that is also very lightweight and durable, and is also used to make rackets, golf clubs and the frames of racing bikes. It can also be mixed with other materials, for example to produce even stronger, lighter tennis rackets or bicycle frames.

Figure 5.41 Graphite is an excellent material for tennis racket frames because it is light but strong

Carbon fibre-reinforced ceramics

This material is used in Formula 1 racing-car brakes. It has great properties of the different materials that make up the composite. It can withstand temperatures of over 2000 °C, but is much lighter than a metal. It has better grip and its frictional properties last longer. This means that braking distance is reduced, the brakes last longer and the car is easier to drive. All this will reduce those precious seconds on the lap time.

Wood and synthetic composites

Skis are made from a mixture of wood and synthetic fibres, or a composite of wood with a foam injected into it. Different types of wood are useful for different reasons. The spruce tree has long-fibre wood that is light and flexible; the fir tree is more dense and is used for its strength. Manufacturers blend the two woods to gain a balance of the benefits of both. Hockey sticks are made from a combination of wood, carbon fibres and fibreglass, or composites of graphite and KEVLAR®.

There are advantages and disadvantages of both types of material, and materials scientists use a mixture to get the best properties for the best performance.

Synthetic versus natural – which is best?

Materials scientists use a combination of both natural and synthetic materials to obtain the best properties. The best materials in new sports developments are composites of natural and synthetic materials.

34 Describe the properties of 'sports wool' that make it ideal for football shirts.

35 Give two materials that make up modern football boots and state why they are used.

36 What materials would you use to make a new tennis racket? Explain your choices.

37 Explain why composites are so useful in sports equipment.

Practical Work – Investigating the tensile strength of materials

Materials scientists carry out simple tests such as these on new materials made in the laboratory. If a material has a high tensile strength, it is very strong. You can test the strength of a material by seeing how much mass can be hung on it before it breaks.

Equipment
- Clamp stand and clamp
- G-clamp
- Crash mat
- 100 g masses
- String
- Small amount of cardboard
- Selection of materials to test (a variety of synthetic and natural materials)

Procedure
1 Cut a strip of material 25 cm long and 1 cm wide.
2 Set up the equipment as shown in the diagram.
3 Measure the length of the material before attaching the 100 g mass.

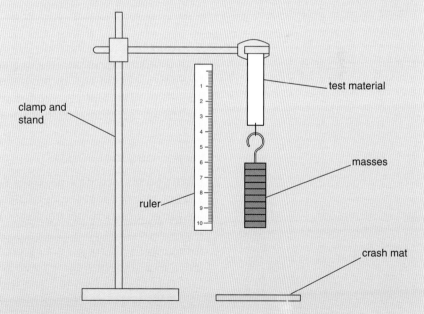

4 Add on 100 g mass and record the new length.
5 Repeat this until either the material breaks, or the material doesn't stretch any more.
6 You need to record your results in a table.

3.4 Forces in sport

For the Unit 2 written exam you need to:
- explain why friction is important in the design of sports equipment (grip on soles of shoes, aerodynamics of cycle helmets).

You should also be able to use data, theories and explanations to:
- select appropriate materials for sports clothing, equipment and footwear and explain why the different properties are important.

There are many different forces acting on an athlete, including gravity and friction (water resistance and air resistance).

Friction

Friction is a force felt when two surfaces rub together. This can be useful, for example when an athlete pushes against the ground in order to move forward – but it is not useful during the race, as friction from the air (air resistance) can slow the runner down. In fact, the faster the runner moves, the greater is the force trying to stop it. The developments in new materials are often about trying either to reduce the effects of friction through air resistance or water resistance, or to increase friction through grip, for example in gloves, tyres or running shoes. The amount of friction depends on the material and the mass of the object.

Without friction, it would take nearly 6 hours for a car to accelerate to 30 mph on a level road.

Air resistance can affect any athlete who moves through the air, such as high-jumpers, sprinters, skiers and cyclists. It also affects any equipment that moves through the air, for example football, tennis and the discus. The same is true for swimmers, rowers and sailors, who experience resistance from the water.

Friction and motor racing

Have you noticed how different racing cars have different shapes? Taking into account the wonderful world of physics, the wider the car, the faster it goes round corners – exactly what is needed for racing.

If there were no forces acting on a moving car, it would continue to move in a straight line. A force is needed to change the direction of the car. This force is friction. The friction between the car tyres and the track makes the car change direction or curve round, and helps to keep the tyres on the track. The speed of the car also has an effect. If the car is going too fast, the frictional forces are not enough to hold the tyres onto the track, and the car spins out of control.

Figure 5.42 Formula 1 racing cars are designed for speed and have an aerodynamic shape.

Down force
The downward pressure created by the aerodynamic shape of a racing car

The tyres of racing cars are much wider than normal tyres. They are also called 'slicks' because they don't have any tread. This increases the area of tyre in contact with the track, which increases grip during cornering. Tyres can heat up to temperatures of over 90 °C during racing, but the new materials used can withstand these temperatures, and the surface of the tyres becomes more like a gel than a solid. The weight of the car, together with the '**down force**' created by the wings, pushes the tyres into the racetrack surface, giving more friction and greater grip during cornering.

Figure 5.43 Normal tyres with tread (left). Tyres with no tread are used in racing to improve handling on corners (right).

Practical Work – Materials and friction

A series of short practicals to investigate the force of friction. Materials scientists carry out simple tests like these on new materials made in the laboratory. You can test the force of friction using a newton meter, which measures how much force is being exerted on the material. The higher the force, the larger is the number on the force meter, which means the greater the force of friction.

Equipment
- Range of newton meters
- Wooden block
- Selection of materials – suitable size to fit around the block
- Ramp or surface of some sort to pull the block across

Procedure
1 Set up the equipment as shown in the diagram.
2 Using the force meter, gently pull the wooden block along the surface of the ramp or surface.
3 Record the force of friction.
4 Attach a material to the underside of the block, as shown in the diagram.
5 Using the force meter, gently pull the block along the surface of the ramp.
6 Record the force of friction in a table.
7 Repeat this for a range of different materials.

An extension of this practical could be to change the surface of the ramp – what happens if the surface is covered in sand, water, or even ice?

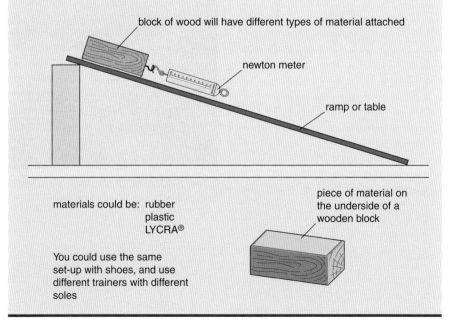

block of wood will have different types of material attached

newton meter

ramp or table

materials could be: rubber
plastic
LYCRA®

You could use the same set-up with shoes, and use different trainers with different soles

piece of material on the underside of a wooden block

Aerodynamics
The study of how a fluid (such as air or water) flows round an object when it is moving

Drag
A force that opposes movement, sometimes called air resistance

Aerodynamic shapes

Objects with a uniform shape, such as a football, move through the air quite slowly because air particles do not flow past the ball in smooth symmetrical lines, but form eddies behind it, which slow it down. **Drag** forces increase with speed. Two of the main sports affected by air resistance are cycling and motor racing. New cycle helmets and racing bike designs minimise the area of the cyclist in contact with the air to try to reduce the amount of drag, and helmets have elongated shapes that also reduce drag.

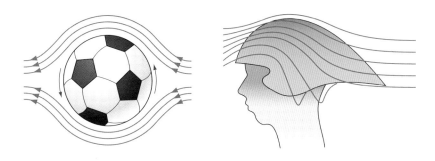

Figure 5.44 Shape is the main factor that affects air resistance.

New racing bikes are made from lightweight carbon frames, with handlebars that tuck underneath the cyclist to become more streamlined. Look at the pictures below and try to identify all the differences between the two bikes.

Figure 5.45 What are the differences between these two bikes?

Car designs

Aerodynamic design to reduce drag has played a major role in the design of racing cars for many years. In the 1960s, inverted wings were introduced on the back of Formula 1 racing cars. The wing could be

Figure 5.46 Upside-down wings on the back of this racing car produce down force when the car is moving.

moved during the race. Today, car manufacturers use wind tunnels and track testing to investigate the effect of different aerodynamic shapes on the drag created behind the car.

The Winter Olympics – the luge

The physics of ice is a science by itself. Why do curlers brush the ice? How does it feel to be travelling down the ice track at 85 mph, head-first, in the skeleton bob? The luge is one of the most dangerous sports in the Olympic Games, so what does it take to finish first?

For the luge, the start of the race is the most important part – a second's delay here could mean 3 seconds added on to the finishing time. The sled's design maximises speed. It is made from fibreglass and steel, and is custom built for each athlete based on their height and weight.

The sled consists of:
- two steels – the only part of the sled that comes into contact with the ice, they are made from metal and are very sharp;
- two bridges – made of steel, connect the runners and steels to the pod;
- two runners – often made of fibreglass, the main steering mechanism of the sled and the curved section – the bow is flexible to allow the slider to steer;
- the racing pod – the fibreglass base on which the slider lies;
- two grips – handles on either side of the pod for the slider to hold on to.

The clothing of a luge slider is also made specifically to maximise speed. The slider wears a full body suit made from smooth, skintight rubber to reduce the effect of drag. They also have special boots that, when zipped up, make the feet point in a straight line, this again reduces the effect of air resistance, as does the shape of the helmet. But the gloves have spikes sewn into the fingertips, which helps to increase the friction between the hands and the ice so the slider can push themselves over the ice at the start of the race.

38 Decide which of these would increase the effect of friction and which would decrease it:
   a) spikes on running shoes;
   b) oil on the arms of football players;
   c) all-in-one body suits for swimmers;
   d) rubber grips on cycle handlebars.

39 Explain why luge sliders have gloves with spikes sewn into the finger tips.

40 Using your knowledge of aerodynamics, state which of the following shapes would be best for a cycle helmet and explain your answer.

a)   b)   c)

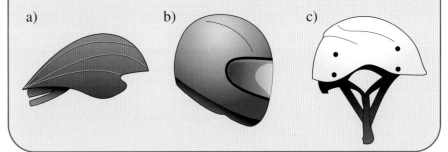

Case Study – Oi, faster!

Scientists develop clothes to push athletes harder

Alok Jha, Science Correspondent

Athletes will try almost anything to find that extra edge: from physical to mental training, you can bet somebody is being pushed by a coach somewhere. But as if pushy coaches were not enough, athletes will now have another tool in their search to shave off those seconds or improve their stroke: pushy clothes.

Scientists in the Netherlands have developed sports clothing with built-in sensors and vibrating pads to let athletes know if they are training at their optimum level. According to a report today in *New Scientist* magazine, the clothes will detect how active certain muscle groups are during training and send back tactile signals if performance drops, reminding the wearer to work harder in that particular area of the body. The scientists say 'the feedback can be understood by the person much more quickly than if they are getting shouts from a human trainer.' Getting faster feedback about their body's performance will mean that athletes will be able to respond more quickly to any changes in their surroundings.

So far, the clothes have only been tested on rowers in a laboratory.

Pads worn at the ankle and the waist monitored the speed at which an athlete moved and how they co-ordinated their body movements. If they lost their rhythm, the pads would vibrate at the correct pace to help the athlete get back on track. These reminders could mean the difference between first and second place.

The researchers have also made vests for speed skaters with vibrating pads at the shoulder and hip. Already being tested by Dutch skating coaches, the clothes provide information on a skater's movements as they move around the racetrack.

Footballers with posture problems who kick the ball in inefficient ways will also benefit from the technology – the researchers are developing remote-controlled clothing that can be operated by managers from the sidelines.

Adapted from *The Guardian* newspaper online, Thursday 29 September 2005

41 Describe what these 'pushy clothes' actually detect.
42 Pads worn at the ankles monitor speed. What happens if the athlete slows down during a match?
43 What are researchers developing for the future?

3.5 Unit 3 Investigation: materials used in sport

In Unit 3 you have to complete at least one investigation for your portfolio. This investigation contributes 40% of the marks to the overall qualification. You will need to carry out an investigation, write a report and explain your findings. This investigation could be used as the basis for your portfolio for Unit 3.

Your report should:
- describe the purpose of the investigation;
- describe how the investigation is connected with a particular sport;
- include a plan and a risk assessment for the investigation;
- make conclusions from and evaluate the investigation;
- explain how a sports scientist might use the results of the investigation.

Remember this is worth 40% of your overall marks.

Your investigation brief

You are a materials scientists working for SportswearUK Ltd. The company is launching a new range of sports clothing, including swimwear and full-body LYCRA® suits for sprinters. The company have asked you to carry out some final checks on the materials to make sure they are suitable for the new range. They are interested the properties of the materials and the effects of friction on the materials. You need to design a range of experiments to test the properties of a range of different materials. Don't forget you need to include a plan and risk assessment for the investigation.

The investigation will take about 3–4 weeks.

What you need to do
1 Plan an investigation to test the materials. You could look at the following:
   - tensile strength of the materials;
   - frictional force of the materials on different surfaces;
   - insulation properties of the materials;
   - cooling properties of the materials.

2 Decide which measurements you are going to take. Remember to think about the following:
   - how will you keep the test fair? (what are the control variables?)
   - will you repeat the tests?
   - how will you record your data?
   - can you make any predictions about what might happen during the tests?

3 What to do with your data:
   - record your measurements in tables and graphs;
   - what do your results show you about the properties of the different materials?
   - how could you make your data more reliable or valid?
   - how could you make your procedure better?
   - how could you use this information to advise SportswearUK Ltd about the materials they have chosen to use?

1 Sports physiologists need to know about the heart and how it works. Copy and complete the sentences below using the key words. You can use the words once, more than once or not at all.

artery   atrium   vein   ventricle

The blood flows into the right _____ and then down into the right _____. From here the blood is pumped to the lungs via an _____. In the lungs the blood picks up oxygen and carbon dioxide is removed. The blood then returns to the heart in a _____ and flows through the left atrium and then into the left _____ before being pumped around the body via an _____.

(6 marks)

2 Athletes who compete in the 100 m sprint are very fit – they have trained their heart and lungs to work hard during vigorous exercise.
a) The pulse rate for two 100 m sprinters was measured. Calculate the pulse rate in beats per minute for the two athletes.

Athlete A	Athlete B
16 beats in 15 s	12 beats in 15 s
_____ beats in a minute	_____ beats in a minute

(2 marks)
b) Which athlete do you think is fitter? Explain your answer.   *(2 marks)*
c) i) During a 100 m sprint, athletes need a lot of energy – this energy comes from respiration. Write the word equation for respiration.   *(2 marks)*
    ii) A lot of heat is produced during respiration. Describe how an athlete can keep their body at a constant temperature.   *(4 marks)*
    iii) Sometimes athletes get energy from 'anaerobic respiration'. What does the term 'anaerobic' mean?   *(1 mark)*
    iv) State two things that happen in anaerobic respiration that are different from aerobic respiration.   *(2 marks)*

3 Getting oxygen into the lungs is really important for athletes. The fitter an athlete is, the slower the breathing rate. This is because they take very deep breaths to get more oxygen in one breath. Describe the process of inhaling.   *(5 marks)*

4 State the differences between arteries and veins.   *(3 marks)*

5 Where in the blood is a) oxygen carried; b) glucose carried?   *(2 marks)*

6 Name a food high in carbohydrate.   *(1 mark)*

7 Name a food high in protein.   *(1 mark)*

8 a) BMI is a measure of the weight and height of an individual, and can be used by sports nutritionists. Look at the BMI chart and the table below, and fill in the gaps in the table.

Underweight	<18.5
Normal	19–24.9
Overweight	25–29.9
Obese	30–34.9
Clinically obese	35–39.9
Extremely obesity	40+
BMI = weight (kg)/height² (m²)	

BMI = weight (kg)/height^2 (m^2)

Athlete	Weight (kg)	Height (m)	BMI	Description
Peter	72	1.78	22.27	Normal
Jill	68	1.68		
Alex	85	1.83		

(6 marks)
b) Alex is a weightlifter. Do you think his BMI score is something the nutritionist needs to worry about? Explain your answer. *(2 marks)*

9 3- and 7-day diet diaries are often used by nutritionists to measure the amounts and types of food eaten. What are the main problems with using diet diaries to measure intake of nutrients?   *(3 marks)*

10 Carbohydrate loading is a particular type of diet that some athletes use just before competing.

a) State a food that is rich in carbohydrates. *(1 mark)*

b) Explain why the glycogen store in the muscles increases after a diet low in carbohydrate followed by a diet high in carbohydrate. *(3 marks)*

c) Some athletes eat a diet that is low in carbohydrate but high in protein.

   i) Name a sport where athletes eat a protein-rich diet. *(1 mark)*

   ii) Explain how the protein is used in the body. *(2 marks)*

11 State the force that acts on runners as they run down the track. *(1 mark)*

12 Sports equipment is made of many different materials.

Material	Properties
Graphite	Light Strong Flexible
Thermoset polymer	Light Strong Rigid
Fibreglass	Tough Reinforced strength Lightweight Can be moulded into shape Can be painted
Foam-injected wood	Light Flexible Can be bent
Carbon-reinforced ceramic	Brittle High melting point

Choose a material you think would be suitable to make the different pieces of equipment below. Explain your answer in each case.

a) Tennis racket *(2 marks)*

b) Skis *(2 marks)*

c) Racing car chassis *(2 marks)*

13 Carbon-reinforced ceramics are used in Formula 1 racing-car brakes. This is called a composite material.

a) What is a composite material? *(1 mark)*

b) What property of the ceramic makes the material good for Formula 1 brakes? *(1 mark)*

c) The blades on the luge sled, called sliders, are made of metal. Draw and label a diagram to show how the atoms are arranged in a metal. *(2 marks)*

14 Sports wool is a special type of material with polyester on the outside and a natural wool-like material on the inside, close to the skin.

a) What are the advantages of having the wool-like material on the inside? *(2 marks)*

b) Fastskin® is a new material used by some athletes. It is meant to reduce the effects of forces that slow athletes down while they are competing.

   i) Who might wear a suit made from Fastskin®? *(1 mark)*

   ii) Describe why Fastskin® is useful to athletes. *(2 marks)*

   iii) What is the force acting on these athletes as they compete? *(1 mark)*

Index